Turn at the Pine Trees

A selection of twelve short stories about growing up in
the North Dublin hamlets of Turnapin, Clonshaugh and
Santry in the late 1960's and early 1970's.

Written and Illustrated by Gerry Cooley

*To Sarah,
my adopted
grand
daughter*

Turnapin Press Company
2011

Publisher
Gerry Cooley

Acknowledgements.
Tar and Cement lyrics Pockriss & Vance.
All internet images are used with all owners rights intact

Photographs courtesy of,
Josie Redmond, Terry Clarke, Doris and Christy Curtis, Chris Duffy, Joan and May Donohue, Cathleen Timmons, Brendan & Eileen Dean, Peader Hardiman, Mrs Murphy, Marie Murphy, Johnny Murtagh, Brendan Scally, Cathleen Moreland, Bernie Roberts, Gerard Cooley (Da).

Special thanks to, Mr Gleeson, Headmaster of Larkhill Boys School & School secretary Betty Murtagh for all her help and time. Terry Clarke for his Photograph and Posters magic. Grace Wilentz for P.R. & Press.

Proof reading: Helen Ryan and Near90fm Team, Ronnie & Zandra.

Ordnance Survey Ireland Permit No. 8767.

ISBN 978-0-9569284-0-5

Illustrations: Gerry Cooley
Cover Design: Gerry & Sean Cooley/Catherine McKenty Fleming.
Design, Layout and Text Design: Sean Cooley
Printer: Woodprintcraft, Coolock , Dublin 17, Ireland

Dedications

To Mary my loving and patient wife who encouraged me
and always told me that I had this book in me.

To my three son's Gerard, Russell and Sean who all played
their parts in bringing this book alive.

A few words by Tony O'Reilly

Gerry Cooley is a very special person, he is a natural aristocrat.

By that I mean, that in his view, all human life is both equal and interesting, what ever it's economic circumstance or geography.

In his case, his passion for Santry and Turnapin Lane,
a small village and townland now submerged in surburbia,
it's people and the evolution of it's history, is vivid proof of this.

His book of short stories is a tapestry of these people,
all set in the surrounds of Santry and Turnapin Lane.

As a young man I often sat in my room in Oakdene on old Coolock lane. As I studied I sometimes looked out of my window across the rolling fields of Royal Oak farm towards that place called Turnapin Lane. I wondered what went on there and now thanks to these wonderful stories, I know, as do we all.

This book is proof of his vision and it's an honour to be a small part of it.

Tony O'Reilly, 2011

Prologue

I was born in the Rotunda in Dublin in June 1958 and spent the first two years of my life in a second floor flat in no 32 Lower Gardiner Street in Dublin's North inner City. The owner of that particular house was a man called Ned Conway. This house was on the corner of Deverell Place that led into Marlborough street national School. It was demolished in the early 1990's to make way for the new generation of urban dwellings called town house apartments. There are 5 blocks in total all along Gardiner street and they are called "Custom Hall." As it happens they are some of the better ones built in the recent building frenzy.

33 Lower Gardiner Street, with Black door

No 33 Gardiner Street lower however is still standing on the opposite corner, a mirror image of no 32. I was baptized in the nearby Pro-Cathedral in Marlborough Street. My younger brother Noel, who is only 11 months younger than me was there with me as well. One story from these years is that my mother used to park my pram outside on the path beside the lamp post "to get a bit of air." I often remind her that this worked well out in the country but not on the paths of busy Dublin streets choked with lead laden petrol fumes! Her answer is, "Pity nobody didn't Jesus take you!"

Prologue

In 1960 my father bought 36 Grove Park avenue and we lived there for just five years. We finally returned to Turnapin lane to live in No 21, my father's family home, when I was the ripe old age of seven. My younger brother Noel, sister Linda, and baby David, just 6 months old made the journey with me. My grandfather Bill Cooley, a widower since 1954, had married again and he and his new wife, Vera Gleeson, along with their first and only child, Sandra, went to live in our house in 36 Grove Park Avenue. It was a straight swap, a win win situation for all concerned.

I am very unusual in so far as both of my parents were born and reared in Turnapin Lane. My father was born in no 21 and my mother in no 33, so it's understandable that I am so attached to the place and the people in it.

I have to admit that I never really liked the name "Turnapin" at all. Whenever I told anyone where I was from, their first reaction was always a double take, so sometimes it was just easier to say Santry or Cloghran. When attending primary school in Larkhill I was in class with lads from Beaumount, Ellenfield and Larkhill.

Early Grove Park photo with cousins, Jackie, Tina, and Susan

When I told them that I was from a place called Tunapin Lane, "Turnip where?" was the usual retort, quickly followed by "More like Turnip Heads," and guffaws of laughter at my expense. Putting the tongue twisting name to one side, growing up in Turnapin Lane was a really special time for me. The childhood years are very different from later

Prologue

years and experiences from this period always linger longer in our memory banks. My generation was the last to be reared in a place that had changed little since the 36 cottages were first built in the early 1930's. The surrounding fields and farms were all the same ones that my parents had grown up with.

Back on a visit to 33 Turnapin Lane circa 1960, Me in Da's arms (on left)

My stories take place between 1965 and 1970 and they bring to life a time in Turnapin Lane before it all changed forever. Turnapin wasn't on its on own when the changes came at this time to Dublin. There were many other small town-lands and villages all around Dublin overwhelmed by a quickly expanding city. Unfortunately we got it from both sides, the city to the South and Dublin Airport to the north. The Airport in particular, being only a mile away from us was a huge influence on the way things would go.

Prologue

If my memory of events aren't accurate do please forgive me. I hope you enjoy the spirit in which they were written. There are small pieces of fiction woven in here and there, but in general most events did actually happen. The names of those involved may be a bit jumbled and the timing may not be altogether correct. Some events have been combined to create a good narrative. Sadly a few of my childhood pals have passed away, with some never making it to adulthood. I dedicate these stories to all of them and I sincerely hope their families are pleased with this.

I didn't move very far from Turnapin, as I have spent the last twenty five years living close by in Santry. My wife Mary and I chose to rear our three sons in this area and they all attended Larkhill national school just like me. My ties have remained close and with my parents Gerard and May still living in no 21 to this day, I have always been literally within walking distance of these childhood memories.

In the past 5 years however, the room where these memories abide has been getting a little darker, smaller and a little more distant. People in particular are slipping away quietly. The door to this room is closing slowly and its harder to get back in there now. These stories are my attempt to put a foot in this closing door, to push it back open, even if only for the shortest time.

On one level they are a celebration of a happy, busy and shared childhood, but on another, its a little bit like me saying goodbye. There you have it. I have finally put them down in print and saved them for posterity. Please join me on the journeys and adventures, I know you will enjoy them. Read my stories at your ease and I hope you appreciate my sketches of some places that have long since dissappeared and vanished forever with no photographs to look at.

Prologue

I have placed the stories in chronological order as best I can. This is not the "Angela's Ashes" of Turnapin Lane. Yes, there was poverty and hardship for some, but along with all of this there was hard work, fun times, great neighbours and friendships.

I offer up these stories as a small source of nourishment and encouragement in these times of unease and unrest in our bewilderingly complicated society. Be calmer for the reading, knowing that that there is a latent strength and nature in us all that will carry us through in the end.

Back living in Turnapin Lane, Uncle Christy (Ma's brother) comes to visit. Me, Noel, Linda and baby David, sitting on aunt Chris's lap

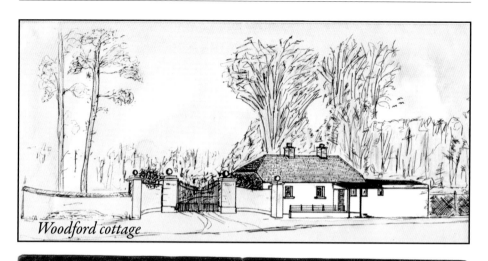

Woodford cottage

In Loving Memory
of

JOHN KAVANAGH

Turnapine Lane, Cloughran

who died on

12th February, 1949

Aged 73 Years

Sweet Heart of Jesus be Thou
my love.—*300 days indulgence.*

Sleep in peace, O dearest Father,
  Thou art happy, thou art blest,
Earthly care and sorrow ended,
  Nought to break thy holy rest.
Never did a heart more faithful
  Throb within a human breast,
Than the one now stilled for ever,
  Passed into eternal rest.

For many years the family chain
  Was closely linked together,
But oh ! that chain is broken now,
  The main link gone for ever ;
The sunshine of our happy home
  Must ever clouded be,
But Thou, O Lord, Who sent this
    cross,
  We bear it all for Thee.

Sacred Heart of Jesus, I place my
trust in Thee.—*300 days indulgence.*

CENSUS OF IRELAND, 1901.

(Two Examples of the mode of filling up this Table are given on the other side.)

Introduction

Just for the record I can go right back to 1882 when my great grandmother, Catherine (Kate) Nagle was born in the townland next to Turnapin Lane called Dardistown. Her parents were John and Annie (Murphy) Nagle both from Cork.

The Nagle cottage where they once lived is still standing today. It is the one facing the College of Surgeon gates with the beauty board clad porch on the front. It is now owned by a car hire company and it now stands closed and silent, waiting for it's evitable demolition.

I wonder what my relations "The swanky Nagles" would have thought of that? By the 1901 census Kate had moved into "Turnapin Lane" with her new husband John Kavanagh, who worked as a plough man in the locality. They were living in Woodford Cottage, also known as Carleys Lodge. William Cox was in residence in Woodford House at this time.

By the 1911 census they are in Stockhole, known locally as Leavy's Lane with three daughters Jane, Annie and Julia (Sissy). My grandmother, Cathleen, the youngest girl wasn't born until 1913. Working in Castlemoate and Dawsons as a plough man, Tom Kavanagh and his family ended up living back in Turnapin in the 2nd phase of Turnapin Cottages (1934), in no 21 at the bottom of the Terrace.

Kate, my great grand mother never made it to no 21 Turnapin Lane. According to family folklore she died of T.B. and she is buried in the Balrothery union graveyard. By a quirke of ill fate her husband, my great grandfather, John Kavanagh, would be knocked down and killed in 1949 at the bus corner only 20 yards from Carley's Lodge where they had started their married life back in 1901. He was aged 73 years and he was returning from his job as watchman on Saville's new farm machinery premises in Santry.

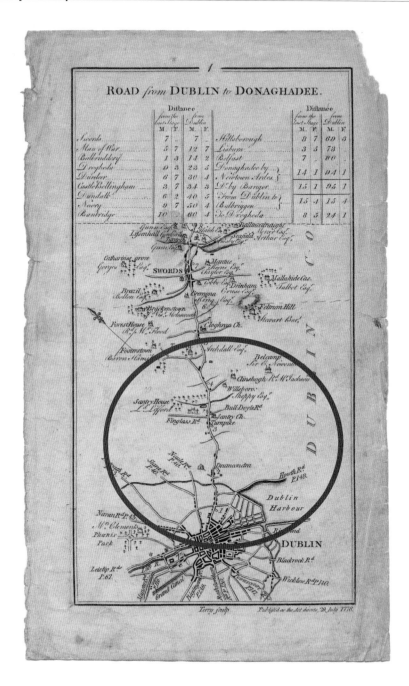

History by Maps

This extract is from the Taylor-Skinner Map first published in 1778 by direction of an Act of Parliment. This is from the "Road from Dublin" section and outlines the road from Dublin all the way to Donaghadee, over 94 miles from the city. As it passes the 3 mile mark in Santry it shows the Turnpike station (toll house) before meeting the turnoff right called "Bull Doyle Rd." This is what we know now as the old Coolock Lane. Passing Santry House on the left we can see that a Lt. Lifford is in residence there.

Interestingly as we move further on we can see the lake in Santry Woods is there, the very same lake my story from Chapter 7 is set in. We can also see the Santry river is feeding the lake and passing under the main road, as it still does today. Moving along we come to the right turn into

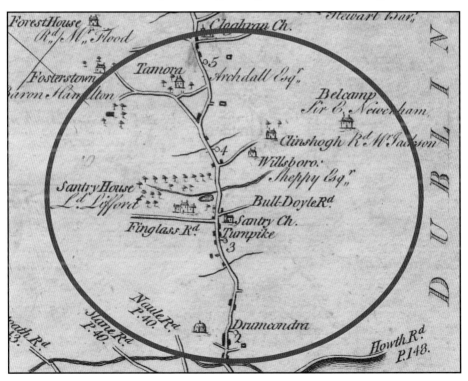

an entrance road into Willsborough house home of Sheppy Esq. This road becomes Turnapin Lane in later Maps. At this corner we also see a residence where Woodford House (Carleys) later stood. If we follow on the main road we meet a small river just above the 4 mile mark, this is the river Mayne, known locally as "McGuirk's" river.

The name Turnapin appears for the first time on Duncan's map of 1821. On this map we see the name Turnapin appearing north of the "big" house "Woodview" later to be called Woodford House. This house would be home to a boy's academy school and later in the early 1900's, the home of tax collector John Carley. The name Turnapin is also assigned to the small bridge on the old swords road under which the river Mayne (McGuirk's) flows. Coming from Dublin to Woodford House on the corner you "Turned at the Pine Trees"* and then headed down Turnapin Lane to Willsborough House.

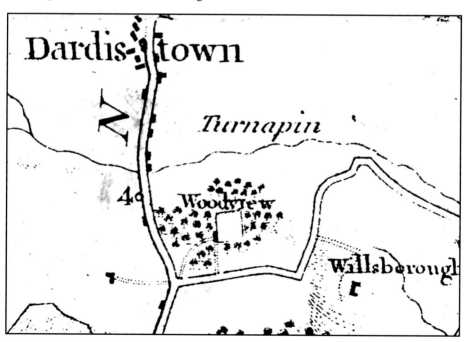

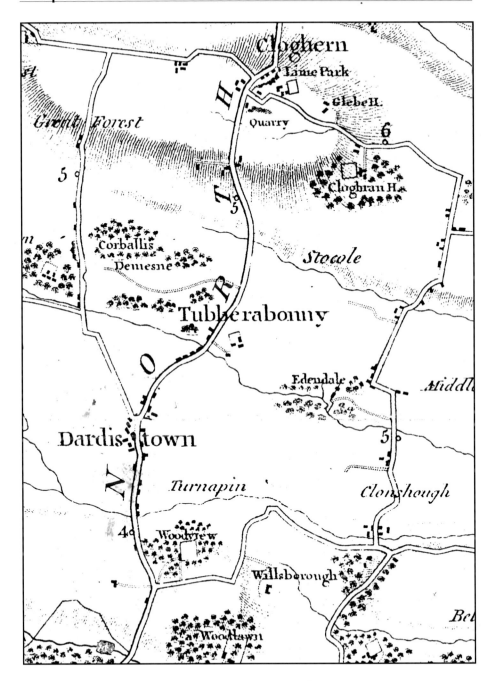

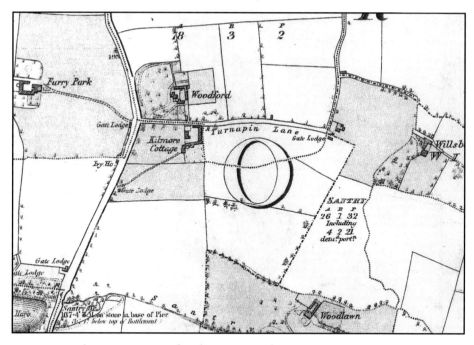

In an 1868 map we see this house standing in McDermott's field with McDermott's old cart road as a back entrance to this house. People familiar with McDermott's field will remember the well in the field with a raised area close by, this being the site of the house itself. The front of the House was accessed through where Hillfarm House stood on the corner. By 1910, the map refers to Willsborough as being "In Ruins".

Turnapin Cottages themselves were built between 1932 and 1934, in two stages, 20 in 1932 and a further 16 in 1934. These were built on land fomerly the Jolly estate, now know as McKennas'. We never called the place Turnapin Cottages, it was always Turnapin Lane to us. These cottages appear for the first time on the Ordnance Survey map of 1936. Worth noting on this same map is the "Santry Park Athletic Grounds" situated north of Turnapin Cottages. This would later become Currans.

Map   : Ordinance Survey 1910

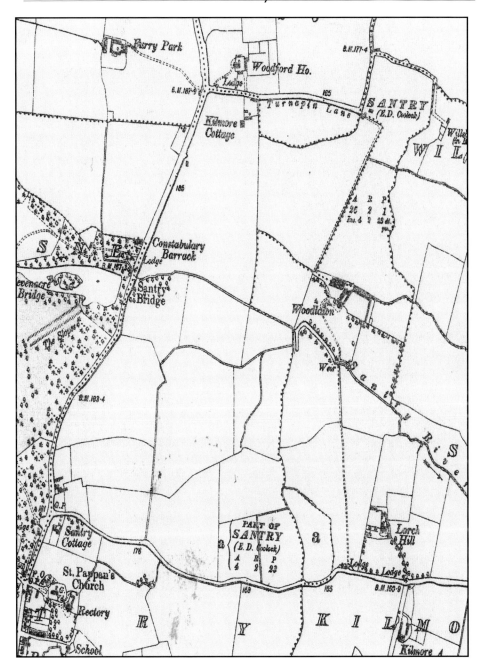

Map : Ordinance Survey 1936

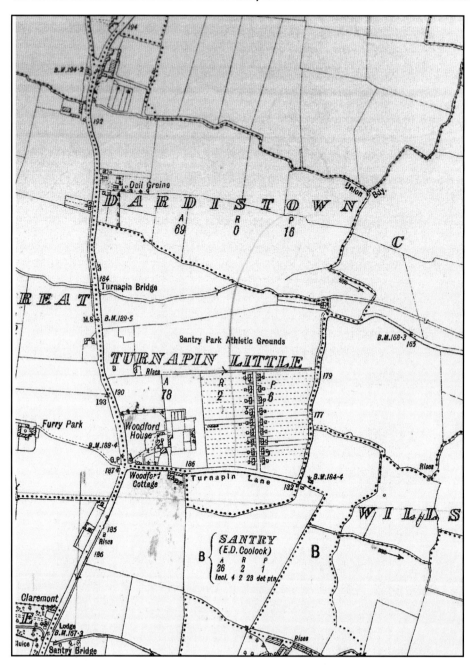

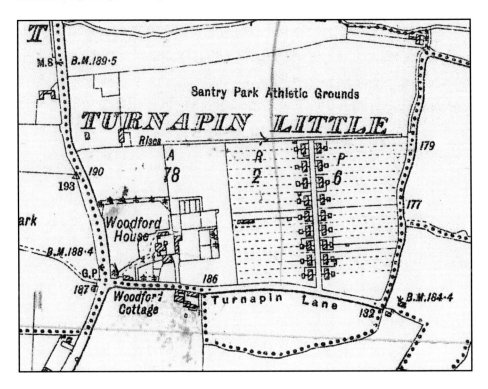

One theory on the name Turnapin is that it came from it's original Irish name being " Thor/Tobar na Binn/Bonn" meaning "The Well/Tower of the little Hill". This tower was more than likely a windmill tower similar to one that stood in Santry Village approx facing the Omni Park at the entrance to Lorcan. The well could possibly be the one in McDermott's field close to the site of Willsborough House. The "Hill" is probably what we see today as the "Barrack Hill", which is now part of the main road and starts to climb at the "Little Venice" restaurant. This was the old R.I.C. Barracks, burnt in 1921 during the War of Independence.

The reference to "Little" however does survive to modern times as Turnapin is divided to this day as Turnapin Great and Turnapin Little on Ordnance Survey maps.

Table of Contents

CHAPTER 1

Picking Mushrooms in Geraghty's Field

I have a vague recollection of my father leaning into my bed to quietly wake me up to go picking mushrooms with him. I got up slowly, trying not to wake my younger brother David as I moved over him in the darkness. We slept two up two down in our bunk beds, me and David on the top with Noel and little Stephen on the bottom. The ladder down was always freezing cold first thing in the morning. This particular morning the field mushroom season had just started, so it was early rising to catch them popping up as the morning daylight brought them bursting into our world. It was very important to be first. Forget the early bird catching the worm, it was the early riser getting the mushroom!

Picking Mushrooms in Geraghty's Field

The mushrooms themselves put it up to you as well. "Come and get us quickly" they seemed to taunt us. "Come and get us before we get maggoty," and just to explain that if a field mushroom is left too long in the ground, maggots invade up through the shank into the head. After coming across a few in a lush green patch of grass you picked the first one and checked it. If you broke the shank off and you saw small holes in the head you were too late, the mushroom was "maggoty" and therefore inedible. The maggots had won the race.

The mushroom hot-spots varied from year to year and in the locality around late August, early September, the question on every-ones lips was "aer a mushroom around?" The whereabouts of the mushroom hot-spots were guarded like the third secret of Fatima. If you had stumbled on a good source, it was big-time, "man of the land," "close to nature," "in one with the earth," and all of that guff.

Cliques in the local pubs were formed, with farm labourers and road workers with the County Council becoming the eyes and ears of "The Mushroom Hunters." These would gather quietly and scope the fields of the locality in the early morning mists based on tip offs from their various sources. People only told people they liked. Sometimes a favour would be repaid with the information on the latest mushroom find. By the same token leaving someone out and not telling them was a veiled "get even" act and settling an old score. You knew where you stood if you were kept in the dark about the mushrooms. Some people carried grudges from year to year. "Kept that one quiet, we'll see next year, it's a long road, good enough to talk and drink with, but not to share the word on the whereabouts of the mushers!"

People got great mileage out of winding everybody up, exaggerating the finds and telling lies about the locations. Someone would put the word

Chapter 1

out that "The back field in the wood is full of mushrooms," or maybe you would hear, "Howard's field is white with them." All lies of course spread about to throw people off the scent. If someone was travelling to a "real" find, the car or bicycle would not be parked anywhere near it. The mushroom hunters would spot it and the word would be out. Being in the know about mushroom locations gave you power, a sort of status in the locality, especially the pubs. Mushroom info was always worth a few pints.

In general there was a mushroom "code" that governed the picking. If you came to a field and some one was already there, you kept as far away as you could, without actually leaving the field. You established your patch by walking a big circle and then walked in ever decreasing circles towards the center. No one could claim a whole field. Walking slowly you skimmed lightly ahead of you with your front foot, making sure you didn't stand on any. If you did, that was it, it was instant death! You never admitted that you had stood on a young mushroom, you just moved along and hoped someone coming behind you didn't notice.

If the mushroom was too small you left it and within an hour or so, it would be a big beautifully formed perfect mushroom. Unfortunately this meant that you had to linger on in your spot, walking and hanging around and if you think a watched kettle never boils, trying watching a mushroom grow for a few hours!

The Mushroom Stalk.

Instructions:

1. Procure and Cut a Long grass stem approx 18" Long.
2. At thickest end Sharpen to a point.
3. Pierce and slide each mushroom onto grass stem.
4. Ensure bigger ones go on first. These will rest against Seed head of grass stalk.

Mushroom Varieties:

Ⓐ Table Mushroom: Agaricus Bisporus.
Ⓑ Shiitake: Lentinula Edodes.
Ⓒ Penny Bun: Boletus Edulis.
Ⓓ Giant Puffball: Calvatia Gigantea
Ⓔ Field Mushroom: Agaricus
Ⓕ Morchella: ∼. Campestris.

Chapter 1

Once you left the field, your spot and claim was forfeit and gone. Claim "jumpers" were always on the sidelines, watching and waiting. One name springs to mind as an avid mushroom picker and her name was Annie Caul. She was living in Turnapin lane at the time and you would cross into her patch at your peril. One glaring, long distance glance from our Annie and you were transfixed, just stuck to the spot, come no further, as she waved her arm saying "These are mine."

This one particular year, Da had come back all excited and got me up out of the bed to help him. It was Geraghty's field at the top of Turnapin Lane that had yielded a bumper crop and it was full of them. He had gone out early on a reconnaissance mission and as he passed the field in the early morning mist he could not believe his eyes. They were everywhere. He filled what "Mushroom Stalks" he could, but they were just too many. The most you could get on these grass stalks was about a dozen Mushrooms, any more and it got too heavy. The grass head on the stalk that kept them from sliding off would just give way and break. The most full stalks you could carry would be four, two in each hand. Grass stalks were not the answer for carrying large quantities.

When Da started looking around for something to carry them home in, I picked up Ma's shopping bag. "The very thing" he said slowly, "The very thing" his eyes glazing slightly and a sort of evil smile formed in his mouth. Out the back door quietly and still under moonlight, we headed down our back garden towards the back road. Da had folded up the bag just in case we met anybody. The "Mushroom Hunters" could pop up anywhere at anytime. Out on to the back road through Heeney's gap we headed right and walked quickly up to Donohue's corner at Hillfarm house, where there was a big black iron gate into Geraghty's field, our very own promised land.

"It was still very early in the morning and daybreak was just about upon us. A full harvest moon shone directly over Donohue's house and reflected off the roof slates that shimmered wet with the morning dew. The light was bright yet it was still dark, if that makes any sense at all."

Chapter 1

To this day, over forty years later, my father still talks about this. I can still remember the excitement in his voice as we made our way quickly out over Donohue's gate and out into the fields. It was still very early in the morning and daybreak was just about upon us. A full harvest moon shone directly over Donohue's house and reflected off the roof slates that shimmered wet with the morning dew. The light was bright yet it was still dark, if that makes any sense at all.

Da started telling me, again, as we walked along about how he had discovered this treasure trove. "I wasn't even looking at Geraghty's, I was heading into the corner to go out into Monks' back field which was a great spot last year." "Then," he went on, getting a little closer and lowering his voice, "as I was walking along the dividing fence in Geraghty's field I looked in and saw millions of them in the next field." I had moved on a little bit ahead of him because I had heard the "millions of them" description at least ten times since we had left the house only five minutes earlier. Da helped me over the fence into the field throwing the shopping bag in after me. I hit the ground running darting here and there calling out "Over here Da, no over there, wait there some right there at your feet." Da raised his finger slowly to his lips, smiling as he did so, saying "Ssshhhhuuuussssshhh, will you shut up, or you will have the whole terrace out on top of us." I calmed down and both of us started to fill the bag. In no time at all it was full and bursting at the seams.

It was on the trip back, now in broad daylight, as we were walking down the terrace carrying our shopping bag that we met Da's pal and shooting buddy, Michael Caul. "Jayzus Ger, where did you get them?" Michael asked him. Da told him but added the rider "Now keep this to yourself and don't let the sister Annie know or that's it, the field will be cleaned out in five minutes flat."

Picking Mushrooms in Geraghty's Field

"They are in Monks' back field Michael, millions of them." When I heard this, I looked at Da, just about to correct him about the field, but knew right away when my father winked at me that I was to keep my mouth firmly shut. I admired his cunning, but in reality Da was now suffering from the mushroom "Fever." Then along came Christy Curtis another one of the Turnapin shooting club. Christy was a bit of a Dublin city slicker who always wore all the shooting gear, camouflage jacket, the boots, the hat and with the "broken" shotgun over his arm. He looked like he was going to the Vietnam war rather than Santry Woods.

Both of the men doubled back to their respective houses to spread the word. Michael gave a shout into his younger brother Patsy "Faygo" Caul to get up and get going for the mushrooms. Patsy brought along Michael's son, young Michael for the mushroom picking experience.

Eugene's bar Santry
L to R, Gerard Cooley,
Michael Caul, Kevin
Wade, John Cooley,
Frank Herbert, Billy
Pepper, Bill Murphy

Chapter 1

Michael and Christy weren't really interested themselves as they were heading up to the "Wood" to shoot a few rabbits. My father once told me that Michael Caul would shot anything flying or walking once he got on the hunting trail. Da and Michael grew up together and according to him, Michael was one of the best pub "Ring" throwers in North County Dublin. They both played for the Starlights GAA team together.

By now the word was spreading like wildfire. Jesus it was like a scene from the "Quiet Man" film. People were walking, running, jumping up onto bicycles with bags flapping and dogs barking, all heading for Monks' back field.

To 33 Turnafin Cottages

Now that the jig was up, Da sent me up to my Grandad Bolands in no 33 to wake him up and tell him that there were mushrooms to be got in Geraghty's field. He still had time because everyone right at this moment was heading for Monk's back field. This gave a full hour before

Picking Mushrooms in Geraghty's Field

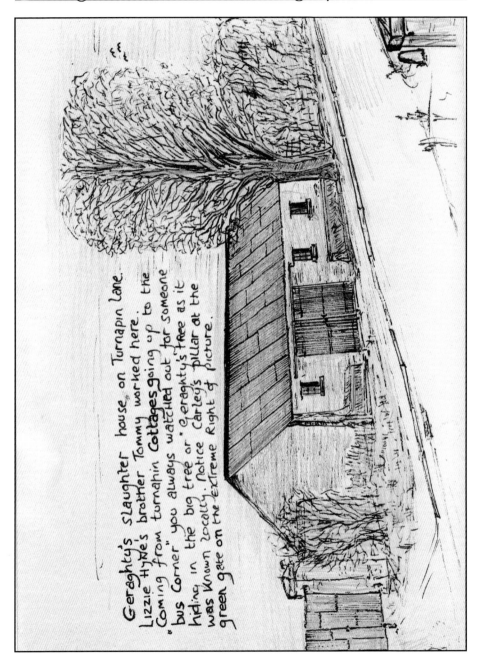

Geraghty's slaughter house, on Turnapin Lane. Lizzie Hyde's brother Tommy worked here. Coming from Turnapin Cottages going up to the "Bus Corner" you always watched out for someone hiding in the big tree or "Geraghty's tree as it was known locally. Notice Carley's pillar at the green gate on the extreme Right of picture.

Chapter 1

the real field would be discovered. I knocked at his bedroom window, which was at the back of the house and he came to the window pushing the curtain to one side cursing loudly, "Who in the name of Jayzus is that?" sticking his head out, with his big red early morning face and his ginger-grey moustache filling the opening in the window. He spotted me and broke into his hearty laugh as he recognised me.

I gave him the message and within two minutes he was sticking his head into the rainwater barrel at the back of the house and pulling his trousers on over the long-johns at the same time. "Holy Jayzus" he shouted "are we Jayzus mad in this place or what?" Although he was now in his mid 60's, he was still a huge man, with the neck, chest and shoulders of a weight-lifter. I left him to it and raced home to Da and the mushrooms.

After all the getting up, walking, climbing gates, jumping ditches, and the picking was over with it was now cooking time. Da was and still is a great cook. His mother had died when he was just thirteen years of age so he became the "house cook" of sorts in no 21. With mushrooms he had three cooking methods, boiled, fried or gas roasted.

The best for me was fried. This was instant gratification. Starving after a few early morning hours in the fields, you would have eaten the odd very small mushroom raw, just to take the hunger off you. The pending fried field mushroom feast was worth waiting for, everyone joined in, oh yes, it was heaven.

The "Rale McCoy" as they say in North County Dublin. Ours were fried up with a few of Dolly Madden's fresh eggs, a mug of tea and buttered bread. Nothing like it, plenty of salt, Jesus they were lovely. Then there was boiling the Mushrooms. This was Da's speciality. Big flat mushrooms in milk, pepper and butter, with a little flour.

Picking Mushrooms in Geraghty's Field

The smell was incredible and the taste even better. Here have a taste of this" he would say "just take a bit and see what you think" and wow what a taste it was and again the buttered bread to soak up the juice. His third method was a tricky one. This ran, while either of the other two methods were in progress.

This was to grill-roast on the gas flame itself. He would turn the gas down low and place a single mushroom directly on it. In the center was a dollop of butter, pepper and salt. The juice would gather in the center as it cooked. The trick was not to burn the mushroom or to spill the juice before you got it piping hot into your gob!

Da usually succeeded, all done with the mushroom sitting on the flat of the knife instead of a fork because the juice would just flow out through the fork holes. After a week however, everyone would be just all mushroomed out and the mere mention of a mushroom would be enough to send the stomach across you sideways. Time, however heals all and when the season hit the next year, all would be forgotten, except for the traitors who never told you where the mushrooms were the previous year.

Postscript: Isn't buying mushrooms today a very boring affair. Upto the Supermarket, get your plastic covered sealed punnet, get in the queue and everybody looking glum and hassled. Scan them out, pay for them and then home. Only when I get the smell as I cook them does all of the above flow back to me, long live the field Mushroom!

In 2006 I managed to get picking mushrooms again with my father at Downpatrick head, County Mayo of all places. He still hasn't lost his touch with the cooking.

Starlights (mid 1960's)
B.Row L-R : A.Dunne, C.McGauley, G.Casey, S.Murphy, N.McCann, C.Hanley, G.Cooley, K.Wade
F. Row L-R: J.Moran, R.Caul, S.McDermott, D.Byrne,T.Dunne, M.Caul, T.Cronin, S.Cronin

CHAPTER 2

The Ghosts of Christmas Past

Everyone has their very own first Christmas morning memory and mine was at the age of six getting a blue tricycle, while my brother Noel got a red one. The way the Christmas tree lights and tinsel, sparkled and shimmered as they reflected in the chrome of the two tricycles has stayed with me to this day. We were living in Grove Park avenue at the time and it would be the last time I would creep down the stairs on a Christmas morning. By the following year we would be living in No 21 Turnapin cottages, which was a single story cottage and it had no stairs.

"The obedient lorries sat waiting, stacked to the hilt with coal, their headlights peering like two twinkling eyes in the blackness."

Chapter 2

Out to the back of No 21 was our small coal-yard and at Christmas time it was very busy and the pace was hectic. What a great place it was to be at that time of year. These were dark and cold frosty mornings, with lorry engines starting up and left ticking over while last minute cups of hot tea were dispensed by my long suffering mother in our very small kitchenette. The obedient lorries sat waiting, stacked to the hilt with coal, their headlights peering like two twinkling eyes in the blackness.

In the big shed there were big overcoats heating up in front of the glowing pot belly stove as the steering directions were shouted out, in the misty, fume laden morning air. We lay half awake getting ready to rise for school, hearing muffled voices shouting "Hard on your left, down on your right", followed by "Whhoooaah, just a little bit on, Grand, that will do you." Back then, when the weather closed in and it got really cold, the coal merchants literally keep people alive, especially the older ones. I always felt important because of this.

In the 1960's the coal business was very much part of the build up to Christmas. Everyone in Turnapin and elsewhere made sure they were kept warm with plenty of coal, logs and turf piled up out in their coal houses. In Turnapin the coal house was next door to the dreaded outside toilet. I still have nightmares about these spider infested hell holes but more about them later. To this day I still meet people who tell that me that the Cooleys' always threw in the coal and no one was ever left cold for the sake of money. At Christmas time all five Cooley lorries were flat out. We had three "Tipper" lorries drawing coal from boats into the city quay coal-yards of Dohertys, Donnellys, and Tedcastles. The other two lorries were the "Bell" lorries which delivered coal far and wide out into North County Dublin. Coal was a cash business, so there was always plenty of money about with Christmas boxes flying in our direction when we went out helping on the coal round.

The Ghosts of Christmas Past

My Grandfather, Bill Cooley always looked after us when he knew we were heading off on the big Christmas "excursion" into town. Yes, back then we refered to Dublin as just town. We would do a little bit in the coal-yard, bagging some bags of slack using the screen to sift the slack off the coal and he always made sure you got paid for your bit of work. In the early days it really was a big family outing into town to see "Daddy" Christmas, and then we were dragged around the shops for the annual Christmas "Rig-out" of new clothes.

This was always a very fretful and traumatic affair, with at least one or two us ending up half strangled in places like Fitzpatricks Shoe shop in O'Connell Street or Boyers in North Earl Street. To this day I remember some of these incidents. They are buried deep in my subconscious such was the brutality and stress of it all. My mother was the poor unfortunate "Pied Piper" with her younger sister Chris giving a "dig out" if you pardon the pun. The word "guzzeled" comes to mind and pretty much described these public chokings and as the eldest I got blamed for everything.

The Look You Like Fashioned by Holmes

Goliath crocodile in black, brown, yoko wine and eucalyptus, also brown/white mocpython £4-15-0

Fitzpatricks

OF DUBLIN

GRAFTON ST. HENRY ST. O'CONNELL ST. GEORGES ST.

Chapter 2

The Del Rio's cafe facing the Abbey was the usual finishing spot for the exhausted, crying, and sulking Christmas shoppers. Here we had our "Christmas" fish and chips. It was handy for us as it was only around the corner from our 41A bus-stop on Eden Quay. One Christmas we all got too much for Mr Del Rio. When he asked my mother to exercise some control over us, she duly grabbed us all together, told the bemused Mr Del Rio, what to do with his "F'ffin" chip shop and promptly left. Subtlety wasn't and still isn't one of Ma's strong points.

I had to be careful on bus journeys as I got travel sick very easily and to be honest I got absolutely zero sympathy for it. In fact I do remember throwing up once on a bus only to get a belt around the ear from my mother for my trouble. "Making a show of me, Jesus what is wrong with you" she rasped. I tried to explain, white faced and coughing through the choking cauldron of fumes, tobacco smoke and vomit, but nobody was listening. I think my brother Noel secretly enjoyed my travel sickness problems.

The Ghosts of Christmas Past

One Christmas however, at the ripe old age of 11, my childhood died when I found out that it was all just a big lie and there was no magic after all. I was totally and utterly devastated. There was no gentle transition, no explanation to soften the blow. There was no "The spirit of Christmas is still real" story from an indulgent parent or an "Inventory of feelings" as the counsellors say now. No it was very matter of fact, brutal even. Something like "You're a bit hairy to be still believing in Santy !"

My mother had no time for niceties like that but Da was different. I seem to remember he was a bit heart-broken for me and a little peeved that he was just told, "Gerard doesn't believe anymore." Now past that age, I was promoted to chief toy advisor for my younger brothers and sisters, so I went into town with Da in his car to help him while Ma held the fort with the younger ones, Noel (10), Linda (9), David (5), Karen (4), and little Stephen (1).

On this particular trip it was a Sunday morning, because Da worked six days a week on the coal at Christmas time. We drove into town and such was the crowd at the Woollen Mills corner that both of us ended up standing on the Halfpenny Bridge on the River Liffey. That was my first view of the city from this angle, I loved it then and I still love it today. While I stood on the bridge I could see a man in the distance with grey hair, wearing a suit, shirt and tie and dark-rimmed glasses. His name was Hector Gray, a small "bucky" man with grey slicked back hair. His real name was Mr Scott and ironically he was from Scotland. The story was that he changed his name because his parents didn't not approve of his "Mr Cheap" approach to selling fancy goods. The original Mr "pound shop" so to speak. The name Hector Grey came from an Austrailian horse Jockey and Mr Scott duly adopted it.

Chapter 2

This day he was standing in the back of a big white covered van in front of the Dublin Woollen Co. He was roaring and shouting, laughing and throwing stuff out of the van and the people were catching it. Da brought me closer but I was too small now, because we had left the bridge. He lifted me up and then I saw that he was throwing toys at the people. There were mostly men in attendance and they were shouting at him and waving their arms. Most seemed drunk to me, all very noisy and they were shouting " Hector! over here, I want two dolls, one black, and one white." The big man Hector shouted back, "What about, a Doll, a Drum, a kick up the Bum, and a chase around the table, will that do you"? Da asked me about Linda, my younger sister, she was nine. I said, "Maybe a tea set, a doll, and a Bunty annual." I remember we definitely got her a doll and little five year-old David got a cowboy hat, guns in holsters and a rifle with real banging caps. On Christmas morning Noel shoved the barrel of this rifle in my ear and pulled the trigger. BANG! Jesus it hurt and it deafened me for ages. Ma nearly killed him.

View of Halfpenny bridge, see Dublin Woollen Mills on the right

The Ghosts of Christmas Past

We left Hector Grey with arms full of toys and headed back to the car. Just to add that Hector Grey had a few "proper" shops in around Liffey and Henry street. Da was generous with us and if you really wanted it, you got it. This time I got Spirograph and Noel got a Scalextric set. Noel was always interested in cars and lorries, he should have been a mechanic like uncle Joseph. He did go on to be the best lorry driver I have ever seen. He was very big for his age and at just 14 years he was driving one of the Bedford "Bell" lorries in and out of town with Grandad Cooley at his side. Noel always wanted what I got, so the Scalextric set with the two cars was really between us. Thankfully the cars were two different colours. To complete the toy buying it was tea sets and nurses stuff for four year old youngest sister Karen. Youngest brother Stephen was only a tot at the time, just about walking, he could play with his Santy rattler and eat the card board-boxes!

Back on the home front when Christmas was getting close, Ma would decide that a few rooms would need new wallpaper. The sitting room in particular was always being done because of the fire. Don't forget at any one time we would have at least one hundred ton of loose coal heaped up around the yard at the back of the house, so it was very hard to keep the place inside clean. My grandfather Bill used to tease my mother saying it was a race against her to see how much he could sell before she met him half way through a heap as she was burning so much coal in the house. Our back boiler was always being replaced as it used to melt with the heat!

I have a great memory of Ma in the middle of one of her wallpapering runs. She used to wear this three-quarter length pink flowery smock with a zip up the middle. She wore it all the time. She was a big woman and she looked as though she was bursting out of it. Nothing well planned, probably the day before the Christmas tree went up. As usual I was

Chapter 2

helping her. Da was always the first to admit that D.I.Y. wasn't really his strongest point. He had headed to Eugene O'Reilly's up in Santry with his friends, Vinny and Billy Pepper in tow, staying well out of the way. I will paint the complete picture for you. Firstly the coal fire was heaped up, red roaring and roasting. Everyone in the room was sweating. Six kids, plus a dog and a blaring television. Linda was still in her school uniform, annoyingly hopping two small rubber balls off the sitting room walls. Tina O'Brien or maybe Thearsa Heeney was with her. They were both reciting "Antsee balls, balls, balls, King of the Jews, Jews Jews bought his wife, wife, wife, a pair of shoes, shoes, shoes" as the balls bounced and they danced around them. She knew Ma was out of range as Ma stood up on the red formica kitchen table. Our dog Rover, a small mongrel collie was chasing the hopping ball and Ma was up on a table measuring the rolls of wallpaper. I had just pasted one full length of wallpaper on the freezing cold hall floor and had run in quickly so I could give it up to her. I dived under the table, scissors in hand, holding the end to trim it while Ma was trying to stick the wet pasted paper in place. The dog was still barking at Linda, and it now had strips of wallpaper paper sticking in its fur and on its paws. Ma cracked and shouted "Will you get that "F'ffin" dog out of here, I am trying to concentrate, now don't have me to get "F'ffin" down to you. Linda paused and glared back at Ma through her pink Dame Enda Everage styled glasses and ignored her. She continued hopping the ball around the barking dog. She was showing off in front of her friends, very brave indeed.

I still sweat a little when I go through this. Underneath the table I cut the pasted paper, but it was wrong. Ma had gone low from the ceiling, so I cut it too short. As we tried to pull it back off the wall the pasted embosted paper started to disintegrate in her hands. At this point Ma was moving into "Dr David Banner, the incredible Hulk" mode, i.e. "Don't make me angry, you won't like me when I am angry," Too late, Ma had lost it. Snapping in an instant she pulled and tore the paper up. "F'ffing" and "Blinding" as she made a ball out of the strip of wallpaper, Linda was now in grave danger. Thankfully for her she was just out of kicking range as Ma did a "Bruce Lee" type side kick, missing Linda but unbalancing herself as she let fly. I was still under the table, and then everything went into slow motion. I rolled out, bumping into the dog who was now standing motionless, staring up at Ma, and as the ball dropped from his gaping jaws, I saw Ma reflected in his wide open eyes.

I looked up over my shoulder from the paper and paste covered floor and saw a woman tottering on the brink of disaster. Her hair was in a pony tail tied to the top and it too was wobbling as she tried to regain her balance, while threatening Linda with all sorts of physical violence when she got her hands on her.

Meanwhile Karen, Noel and David were sitting crosslegged on the floor arguing over the television blissfully unaware of the possible crushing heading their way. Out of nowhere, my uncle Joseph, who was down in the kitchen making tea, had heard the commotion and just in the nick of time saved us as he jumped onto the shifting table, grabbing Ma and steadied her up. Linda had long since run, along with the dog as Ma got down from the table.

She stepped down to a chair beside the table. She was now safe and thankfully so were we. Work was cancelled immediately and we headed down to the kitchen for a calming cup of tea. The next day we finished the room, but when Ma was wallpapering the hall the following day, she actually fell off the table while talking to Joseph, not watching what she was doing. Ma saw the funny side of it as poor Joseph tried to lift her as she was jammed in the narrow hallway on the floor. Linda survived the incident but the poor dog didn't. Poor Rover had a fit shortly afterwards and died lying on his back, feet up the air. Oh the stress of living with the Cooleys!

Karen and Ma, at the front door of No 21

The Ghosts of Christmas Past

After all the wallpapering, the Christmas tree and the Christmas rig-outs were finished, our Christmas dinner was really something to look forward to. Ma really loved cooking and Jesus did she get plenty of practice. The Christmas dinner was hers. After the toys on Christmas morning we headed off with Da to Mass then on to Grandad Cooley's house for our Christmas morning visit. When Grandad died in 1987, we all started to gather in 21 Turnapin Lane, and still do today. As with all big families there is always one who can't make it along for whatever reason. It really is one of the highlights of Christmas, especially for the grand children who would not miss it for the world. The first thing Ma did before we all disappeared was to move the kitchen table up to the sitting room. Da helped her with this. Then the dreaded "furnace" was lit. With the kitchen table now in the center of the room, at least two unfortunates were going to be in the "hot seat".

One year I was late to the table so I ended up with my back to the fire. The only thing you could do was to bank it down with slack and push the damper plate in so the fire was just ticking over. The Christmas dinner was something to behold. Ma really piled on the food and in an effort to keep cool we drank copious amounts of Taylor-Keith red lemonade. This however filled us up even quicker. When at the table I had to be careful. If I said I didn't like something, at least two of the younger ones copied me and said no, they didn't like it either. Once while Ma was dishing out the cabbage from a five gallon pot during a normal dinner, we both spotted the carcass of a caterpillar on the edge of the pot. Just one glaring glance from Ma stunned me into silence. I looked away and ate the cabbage with gusto.

Ma's Christmas trifle was my favourite and even today she keeps a little bit for me. With all courses complete I hobbled away from the table, sweating and bloated to lounge on the sofa, hoping to get the power in my legs back reasonably quickly. The Christmas day film was "The Greatest Story ever told" and Da really liked John Wayne's few words right at the end when dressed as a Roman soldier he looks up at the dying Christ and said "Truly, this man is the son of God" in his best western voice. In the same film the fact that David McCallum, my "Man from Uncle" hero had played the part of Judas who betrayed Jesus, really did upset me. The Christmas films were all great but none will ever better my ghosts of Christmas past.

Post Script: I have been back to the Del Rios and Tony Del Rio makes the best onions rings in Dublin. The Del Rio family came from Monte Christ, near Naples in Italy. By all accounts Tony's father, Dominic, was a quiet man, so we must have been really bad for him to ask Ma to calm us down a bit. Tony's grandfather Amadeaus "Ted" Del Rio set up the family's first shop over near Mercer's Hospital off Wicklow street in Dublin city.

CHAPTER 3
McDermott's Field

" The town that I came from was quiet and small, we played in the meadows where the grass grew so tall. In summer the lilacs would grow everywhere, and the laughter of children would float in the air. As I grew older, I had to roam, far from my family and far from my home."

These were lines in a popular song called 'Tar and Cement' that Joe Dolan sang way back in the long summer days of the late 1960's and even at the age of 12, the sentiments of this beautiful song were not being lost on me. When I hear it now, it always transports me back to walking up McDermott's cart (car) road, smothered by the scent of the lilac bushes either side and the busy buzz of the bumble bees.

McDermott's Field

There was something about the whole tone of this song that really resonated with me. The words would prove to be prophetic because most of the meadows in and around Turnapin Lane would eventually disappear under carpets of tar and cement.

McDermott's field which was situated close to the backroad at Turnapin Lane, started to get a lot of local traffic as the Turnapin crew began to make our way over to the newly opened Northside shopping centre swimming pool. As the crow flew this was about one mile away from Turnapin Lane. This short story relates to one of the very first times I went there. Our motley crew of bathers included myself, Johnny Darcy, Noel Cooley, Olive Heeney, Theresa Heeney, Linda Curtis , Jimmy Heeney and maybe one two more younger "sprats". These tended to be all our younger sisters and brothers, who you never wanted around especially when childhood romances were blooming.

I would compare this scene to one from the Television series "The Waltons" as we travelled down from Walton's mountain, crossing fields and rivers and finally emerging in the 'big city' at Northside shopping centre where the pool was. We all met up at Darcy's back garden gate which opened out on to the back road, directly across from the entrance to McDermott's car road. The car road was about 300 yards long and it led up into McDermott's field. Mahony's ditch was beside Darcy's gate and it stank to high heaven all the time. A rancid, black oil-like substance oozed and bubbled in this ditch and god help anyone who ever fell in there.

The gathered group included a few girls, and this always upset the apple cart a little, as some of us would be trying a little too hard to impress them. Unfortunately for me and my brother Noel, my

Chapter 3

young aunt, Chris Boland, our 'oft' times babysitter was hanging out the washing in No 33 Turnapin Lane and seen us leaving from the gate. She immediately informed my mother who was waiting for us upon our return. Oblivious to the damage the "tell tale tattler" had done us, we all made our way across the road and up into the car road. It was a beautiful summer's day and early in the morning. eleven o'clock was our usual time so as to avoid the big queues that were the norm in the newly opened swimming pool.

Bottom of Turnapin crew circa 1969 Photograph taken in Cooley's coal-yard in no 21.
Back Row L-R: Paul Curtis, Hubert Brudell, Noel Cooley, Gerard Cooley, Jimmy "Skitcher" Heeney (holding David Cooley) and Chrissie Heeney hiding behind Carmel.
Front Row L-R: Theresa Heeney, Olive Heeney, Linda Curtis, Linda Cooley, Patty Curtis, Veronia Pepper, Anne Pepper and Carmel Brudell.

McDermott's Field

McDermott's car road

Chapter 3

It was school summer holidays so everyone was around to go to the pool. All we needed was our towels, togs and money to get going.

Da usually left us our money but this particular morning my grandad, Bill Cooley had given us a bit extra as he was always giving us a few bob now and then for doing small jobs around the yard. Even though it was summertime he would be in the coalyard at the back of our house, pulling and poking around at something or other. He wore a soft trilby hat and had a lovely mischevious smile. When he knew you were watching him, he would throw the coal shovel over his shoulder and march army style swinging his arms and saluting as he went. When he was in a particulary jovial humour, he would whistle as he went, blowing and sucking air in through his puckered lips giving off a sort of wind blowing sound that he always managed to bend into a song tune. Being from Borrisokane himself "Tipperary so far away" was one of his favourites. When we told him where we are going he said "When you get to the Cock and Rabbit," tell that auld sister of mine, May Bannon, that she owes me for a bag of coal" he laughed outloud, "Tell her I'll see her when I get my glasses" as he caught a few loose coal sacks and flung them up onto back of the old red Thames Trader lorry.

The Cock and Rabbit was an old local name for Clonshaugh going back to when there was an Inn there of that name. May lived in a beautiful small gate lodge over in Clonshaugh with husband Bill Bannon and their family. It was close to Monaghan's shop where we stopped on our way back from the swimming pool, but for some resaon I never ever went in to see her there and by all accounts I missed something really special. It remains to this day one of my biggest regrets. My grandfather's sister and I never met her.

McDermott's Field

We walked up the car road, all bare legged, with us boys in short trousers and the girls in their flowery summer dresses. The nettles or "stingers" as we called them were having a field day so our towels were introduced as protection. The girls looked normal in the towel wraps but we looked really stupid as our towels looked like skirts which caused a lot of giggling along the way. Unfolding towels had revealed rolled up multi coloured trunks, pink togs and bikini tops which were fine inside the confines of the pool but now out in the daylight, looking at them seemed a little bit strange and daring even.

On we waddled through the forest of nettles and thistles, like a small tribe of laughing pigmys. I did manage to get a good nettle stinging on my legs but thankfully Doc leaves and spit sorted it out for me. By the time I got to the swimming pool the stings had turned to white blotches and the pain had subsided. Despite the nettle stings there was a lot of laughing and joking as we climbed over McDermott's gate and of course the older girls made sure they showed off their knickers as they swung out over the bars.

Teasing, tripping and jumping we ran like young foals as we made our way across McDermott's field. The belfry and the tall chimneys on top of McKenna's house, a dark and forbidding building, peeped through the hedgetops to our left as we made our way through the lush meadow. McKennas' always kept dogs so instinctively we listened out for any barking.

Johnny Darcy grabbed Olive Heeney's towel and rolled it up in a ball and started kicking it high up into the air scattering both towel and togs as he ran. Olive made the most of it as she ran after him screaming and picking up her stuff. In the middle of this field we always quickly by-passed a piece of corrugated iron that covered a deep hole that was once was a well. We sensed the danger it presented and none of us ever lifted it, especially with sprats about. We had been told that there was once a big house called "Willsborough house" in this field that was used as an ophranage and the children who misbehaved were throw down the well and on dark nights you could here their ghosts screaming up from this hole in the ground. Oh no, we never dwelt too long there.

Our next stop was the "Devil's hole" which was a green stagnant pool over in the corner of the field. Here we passed a few minutes just standing and staring at the green soupy water. We always ended up throwing in a few rocks and broken tree branches to scatter the crust of horrible scum that lay on the surface. We also tried to splash the girls so as to encourage them to chase us, a sign if they were interested in us or not. The sprats ran around as the bigger lads grabbed them pretending to throw them in. A young Willie Heeney was always a soft target, and poor little "Booney", that was his nickname because of his tendency to cry easily, always got the "I throw you in on the way back, if we don't drown you first in pool". Kids were cruel and still are.

The local story about the pond was that someone had once drowned there as the horse and cart they were on got sucked down in the swampy mud, as the Devil himself pulled them under. To be honest between the well and this pond in this field, especially on greyer darker days I sometimes got the creeps and just ran home.

The pond had one side that faced into McDermott's field, while the other side edged on Fowler's field which I seem to remember, at some stage belonged to Dixon Hanley who lived in 34 Turnapin Lane, just next door to my other grandad Jack Boland in No 33.

McDermott's Field

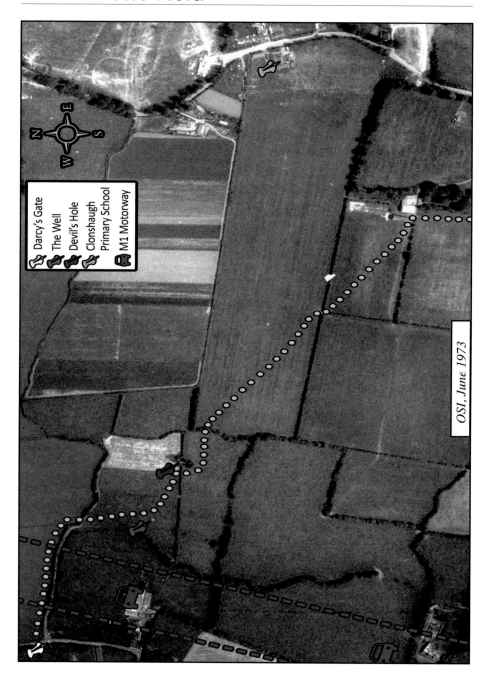

Chapter 3

Just past the Pond we jumped a ditch and on up into the fields at the back of Clonshaugh primary school, which was facing Louie Monaghan's "Back-Shop". Louie had a load of kids, Danny, Mary, Theresa, Sadie, Eamon and Margaret. The older ones helped out in the shop. I would go in there trying to catch a glimpse of Mary Monaghan who I had a bit of a smack for and we usually dropped in there on our way back home if there was any money left to spend.

In the summer the shop was a hive of activity, like a little seaside shop that sold all sorts of stuff. It always had the same smell and that was freshly cut ham and liquorish sherbert. We used to tease Gerry and Derek Madden unmercifully about the way they used to pronounce the word "back" in back-shop. We had a sentence that we would repeat add nauseam. Johnny Darcy would start it and then we would all join in. Johnny would say "Derek Madden is going down to the "Baaack" Shop to get some "Taaa-foe-looks" and then he is going up to the "Post-taaa-fice" to buy a Staaaamp. On and on he went and we thought this was hilarious. Toffo-Luxe were brown toffee sweets that came in a packet like a little red tube. There was about a dozen sweets, all individually wrapped in a plastic type paper. These were so hard that when you chewed them they would pull your teeth fillings out. They were later rebranded to just being called Toffos.

McDermott's Field

Getting back to the trek we turned right into the field at the back of Murphy's house which was called Primrose Park. Betty Murphy lived there and she bred wolfhounds. Sometimes I delivered the milk there with Charlie Hoystead and there would be small wolfhound pups running after me. We walked on a bit towards Murphy's big yard where there was a big shed with round windows set into the back wall. As we walked along the back wall I noticed birds flying in and out of these round windows. When we reached the corner of the wall we got out on to the road just past the red cottage on the left where Rachael Farrell lived. The Brien family were also associated with this lovely little cottage. The granny Brien was known locally as the "Cuckoo" Brien and her son Jack was called the "Jackdaw."

Farrell's cottage on the Clonshaugh road, now demolished.

Chapter 3

As we passed the entrance to a new road of houses in Riverside, we saw Northside shopping centre rising ahead in the distance. On our right I noticed the big gate pillars of Murphys' old yard. Being always inquisitive I peered in and immediately on the right I spotted a little cottage painted a beautiful shade of blue, I wondered who lived there. It looked a little bit like a witches' cottage from an old fairytale.

Betty Murphy's wolfhound stands guard at the old yard cottage. Note the Pups and Cups at the window and the Riverside roofs behind on the right.

Catching up the rest we gathered ourselves into a little bunch for protection as we walked along. We were out of our little bubble now and were regarded as outsiders in this alien concrete jungle. The scene was now moving from the "Waltons" to being a little bit like the "Wizard of Oz" but without "Toto" the dog in our travelling party.

McDermott's Field

Theresa Heeney wasn't happy. She was a quiet little girl who always bit her nails. Maybe she was listening to the exaggerated stories about "Bonnier" (Bonnybrook) as the bigger lads stood to the outside of the group. Maybe she sensed danger, real or imagined. We were all keeping quieter now as not to attract any attention as the "Bonnier" kids had a fearsome reputation. With the midday sun glistening on the new bright concrete glass and steel, Northside shopping centre looked really space age. On we walked down into the hollow over Bonnybrook Bridge, across the carpark to the stairs up to the pool which were on the inside of the centre at the time. The swimming pool sat on top of the centre itself. Immediately we hit a queue about half way up the stairs and the smell of Chlorine hit us immediately as we quietly took our place in the line. Our place in the queue was close to the top so we knew that we would all get through in the next shift. We were early, the rough Coolock kids tended to be around later on in the day.

Northside swimming pool on the roof of the shopping centre

OSI, June 1973

Murphys, Wolfhound's
Farrell's Cottage
Murphy's Cottage
Riverside Estate
Colaiste Dhuilaigh

One young lad in the queue was causing a bit of hassle as he was trying to bring a dog in with him, but he didn't succeed. As we paid our money, little Willie Heeney slipped in without paying. He could share a basket but he needed to get a rubber wrist band of the right colour to make sure he could stay in the pool. I had a red one from the last time, I had kept it, lucky it was a red colour wrist strap group again, so I gave him my spare one. There was always an over powering smell of chlorine in that pool and with no googles we were guarenteed to have the eyes of the living dead on the journey home. Linda Curtis and Olive Heeney were the only two in bikini tops, all others were in the single pieces. Pretty soon we were all in the shallow end, jumping screaming and having a great time, completely oblivious to the "Kaf-fuffle" back in Turnapin caused in no small part by my aunt Chris telling my mother she had seen us heading up the cart road with the girls.

We were all out of the pool by one o'clock, Johnny Darcy, as usual was in trouble over horse play, Linda Curtis was flirting a bit with me, I was chuffed, she lived across the road from me in Turnapin Lane, in her granny Fudee's house in no 15. Linda was very pretty with lovely fair hair. Olive Heeney lived next door to me in No.20 and she was my tom-boy buddy. From our very early years and with us all living at the bottom of the terrace, we were that little bit closer. I remember being gutted when Linda moved away from Turnapin to Santry not very long after this event.

I felt a little bit sick as I had swallowed nearly a gallon of the chlorine laced water, and the home journey was basically a repeat of the in-bound journey. We all dispersed at Darcy's gate and our little group of Heeneys, Cooleys and Curtis's headed on down the back road, turning in at the pump house at the bottom of Heeney's garden. On we came, Heeney's splitting away, leaving me, Noel and Linda Curtis coming up through

60

our yard. Ma was waiting at the door letting Linda pass on and then grabbing me by the scruff of the neck and asking me in no uncertain terms "Where in the name of Jesus Christ were you two?" belting us as we passed her. Chris had told her that me and Noel had gone across the fields with Linda and Olive. She hadn't seen the whole group of about ten, so hasty conclusions were drawn about what we were up to. When I look back on it now, I think how innocent we all were.

Post Script: The only piece of green-space left after all the Tar and Cement brought roads, roundabouts, factories and houses, is just a little tiny bit of McDermott's field.

In this field of thistled hay,
with childhood pals I jump and play,
In hazy sunshine and summer smell
we sometimes peered into that well

I can see it now, in my dreams
a time and place of spring cold streams
Its in the past now, lost in time
but I still visit to see it shine

Noisy scenes of run and shout
with butterflies that dance about
It's time to go, at least for now,
always there for me to smile at.

GC (2000)

McDermott's Field

CHAPTER 4

Summer Days at McGuirk's River

Every now and then from way back in the mists of my early child-hood, my memory flashes brief glimpses of long days spent pottering around at a river's edge. Most of this river has long since been piped under ground, but it was and still is officially called the river "Mayne". It travels under the old Swords road at the very small and little known Turnapin Bridge. This is just past the old entrance to the stock car racing track in Murphys more recently known as the Kart City track. Traveling eastwards under the road it flows on down past Hino Harris's walled yard and then on along by the side of Maddens and McGuirks, the two semi-detached cottages in the above picture.

Summer Days at McGuirk's River

This place was always a huge attraction to myself and the rest of the Turnapin crew. Lads like Gerry, Derek and David "Daithi" Madden, and the young Tommy "Gurky" McGuirk were always around this spot on the river. This wasn't very surprising as they all lived very close by. This small river flowed on through "Barney Boland's" field (owned by Collins) and it ran to the rear of Tinker's corner, then on out into Howard's field. It passed on for about a quarter of a mile through Howard's road field then swung right under Clonshaugh Bridge at the bottom of Jolly's Hill. This is where the tree stood in the middle of the road. It passed directly in front of Roche's big white house and then into the two lakes in front of Belcamp College.

Out in these fields in front of Maddens and McGuirks, the river Mayne met a smaller stream in a ditch coming north from the direction of Williams "small" field. Forans grew cabbage in this field but I not certain if Forans actually owned the field back then or not.

This small field was the place I heard a Cuckoo for the very first time and it was always full of scarecrows who stood silently on guard.

I remember it being a lot higher than the piece of the land adjoining it to the south. This piece of lower land was where we would play our soccer games and was just known as Barney Bolands. Many a time we jumped up into Forans field for a few heads of cabbage for Ma before we headed home to Turnapin. Back then this was normal practice.

Chapter 4

Heading further north along this little stream you crossed on into Collins big field. Leaving Collins land up in the top corner we got through a ditch that brought us into Williams "Big" Field passing a small pond on the left that we called the "Piper's Hole." This was a small swampy pond that we never went near, too afraid of getting "Dragged down to the bowels of Hell and the Divil," as Ned Madden once said.

At the meeting point of this small stream and the Mayne River, just in front of Maddens and McGuirks, a small pond developed and we always called this spot McGuirk's river. As these waters met, it had the effect of creating a widening on both sides and the grazing cattle gathered to drink there. The thirsty cattle churned up the mud banks as they stood and drank their fill. Add in the cow pats, warm weather and billions of flies you were looking at a scene from an African jungle film.

Despite all of this, it was at this spot we spent many a day damming up the river to make it deep enough to swim and float rafts in. We used spades to cut the square sods and one time we got really organised and used a pitch fork to shift the sods around.

As we were cutting some "extra" sods up the end of our garden, in no 21 Turnapin, I took command of the pitch fork. A very young sprat called Paul Curtis, Linda's younger brother, put his foot on a sod just as I was lifting it with the fork. I ran the fork right through his foot, on into the ground pinning his foot where he stood. Ouch! I can still feel it now.

Myself and Paul Curtis

Mrs Foody sitting on logs in number 15 with Carroll's gabel end behind

Young Paul or Pollywobbles as his granny called him screamed the place down, so hard in fact that his grandparents came up our garden to get him and I can still remember his granny consoling him, as she carried him away in her arms. This is my only memory of Mrs Foody, a small thin woman with long frizzy hair. Mr Foody was there as well, but it was his granny who was carrying the injured and crying Paul.

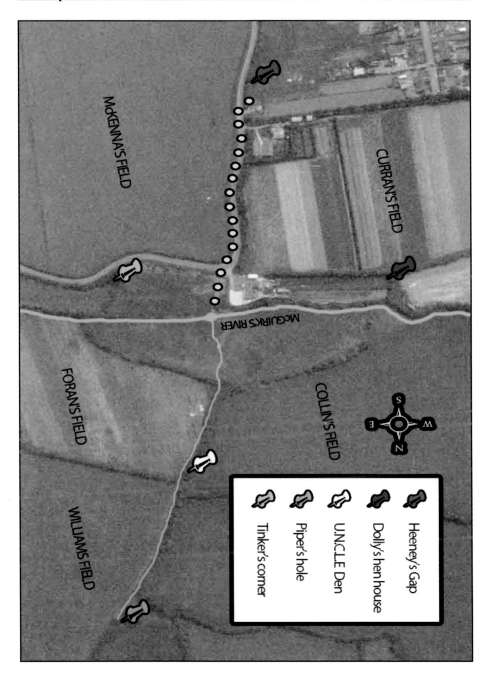

McKENNA'S FIELD

CURRAN'S FIELD

FORAN'S FIELD

COLLIN'S FIELD

WILLIAMS FIELD

McGUIRK'S RIVER

S
E · W
N

🖈	Heeney's Gap
🖈	Dolly's hen house
🖈	U.N.C.L.E Den
🖈	Piper's hole
🖈	Tinker's corner

Summer Days at McGuirk's River

During this incident we had the bright idea of using Mr Farrells old abandoned wheel barrow to cart the freshly cut sods down to McGuirk's river. Our trek was to take us out through Heeney's gap and out onto the backroad. Forward thinking wasn't our strong points as we hadn't counted on Heeney's gap being so awkward and small. Our very first load was very heavy to push and it took four of us to shift it. Anyone who knows wheelbarrows knows its all about balance and momentum. As we gathered speed over the bumpy ground and grass, we now had to get it around the wire fence at the pump house, which was part of Heeney's gap. Heading towards the gap the wheelbarrow was now moving away from us at speed and with the uneven ground underfoot we were all starting to stumble.

Farrell's Wheelbarrow

Chapter 4

The brother Noel was running at the front, he had tied a rope around the front wheel guard and was pulling and running with all his might.

Me and "Skitcher" Heeney were at the back holding the handles up while "Booney" Heeney was adding to the chaos by shouting as he jumped in and out of the moving wheelbarrow.

As you can imagine this was unbalancing us all as we hurtled towards the small right angled gap and the envitable carnage that lay ahead. Skitcher Heeney, holding the left inside handle was first to blink as he started to get jammed between the barrow and the wire pump house fence. He stopped dead as he dropped the handle, but because Noel was going full blast pulling on the front everything was still moving forward and going at speed.

At this stage "Booney" Heeney was now in the barrow and shouting "OH NO, OH NO, Jayzus stop, Mammy Mammy, Jayzus Stop" while holding on for dear life. His fingers were on the top outside edge of the barrow. Just as Noel got to ditch edge, he looked back terrified, dropped the tow rope and jumped out of the way of the approaching wheelbarrow. Booney's fingers got caught on the wire fence so he screamed out as he sat spreadeagled in the merciless, rusty, heavy wheelbarrow as it toppled over into ditch with all hands on deck! We were very lucky the wheelbarrow fell away from us to the left. Booney jumped out, hysterical with pain and fright, running home holding his badly skint fingers. For the survivors it was sore knees, with skint knuckles, shins and elbows along with the usual recriminations regarding blame.

The wheel barrow never made it back out of the ditch and any sods we could salvage out of the "Tomb" were carried down to McGuirk's river in our arms or dragged along on our pram wheeled trolleys.

Chapter 4

Once the dam was in place, it was happy days. It was easier during dry weather because the water ran slower and the dam would hold fast much easier. The deeper the water the better. The McGuirk's river crew were myself, Noel the brother, Gerry "Garter" Madden and his brother Derek nicknamed "Senate". "Hacker" Murphy, Johnny Darcy and not forgetting the oldest lad, "Skitcher" Heeney with his younger brother Willie or "Booney" as we called him.

As always there were the young sprats like David "Daithi La-cha" Madden, David "Crockett" Cooley, Tommy "Gurky" Mc-Guirk with his little brother John. More little brothers like Paul "Herrin'er" Darcy, Dessie "Dick" Murphy, Paul "Fodger" Murphy and lastly little Anto Murphy made up the numbers. My cousins from England, Hubert Brudell and John Boland sometimes made appearances at McGuirks river. Living in built up cities like Birmingham and London, our country side of open fields and total freedom were great adventures for them.

No girls were allowed by the riverbank, no way, too dangerous and anyway "Dam" building was pure 'Boystown' adventure. Sometimes a few girls, including my sister Linda, would gather playing hop scotch at the front of McGuirk's as they visited Tommy's younger sister Martina, but they kept their distance as they giggled and shouted at us while our "Man's work" was going on. Martina was the only girl in the two cottages.

Mr McGuirk, or "MaGoo" as we called him, had mass concreted their front garden so it was ideal for skipping games. He was also responsible for cutting down our very first "look out" tree which grew in front of both of the cottages. Knowing my feelings about trees it will come as no surprise that I didn't really like him after that.

Summer Days at McGuirk's River

As we built the dam the big challenge was to try and keep your feet dry for at least a little while. It was a huge test to see if you could judge the depth of the water correctly before the freezing cold water flowed in over the top of the rubber "Russian" boots. Once the water got in you squelched around for the rest of the day. These boots, however, would eventually have to come off, followed by the socks. Then you went "bare-back" as you put the boots back on and I can still feel the smelly cold muddy water oozing around my toes.

When the water was deep enough, in went the makeshift pallet rafts and at least one half barrel "boat" to float in it. The half barrel was an old empty oil drum cut up the middle and was pretty much useless as it even started to sink with nobody in it.

We only ever had one half a barrel and we only managed to get it about 100 feet down stream towards Tinker's corner before it sank. For years afterwards this barrel lay half submerged in the water and mud, as it silently mocked us and our feeble efforts to master the waves.

No matter what we did it just would not budge. As well as floating rafts we also had designs on swimming in the river once the dam had started taking effect. I vividly remember "swimming" up stream and today I count myself very lucky that I am still alive to tell this tale. You must remember we were down stream from both the meat packers near Hugo Byrnes and Harris's scrap yard, so god only knows what was getting into the river water.

The river was about two feet wide as you crawled upstream on your elbows, buoyed up by the raised water level. It was at the bottom of a very deep ditch, and today, no amount of money would get me near it. When I think of it, as young lads we had no sense of danger at all.

Chapter 4

This one summer we had the "breathing, through the bamboo stick" craze. This was started by the American actor, big Fess Parker who played the part of Daniel Boone in the television series. The trick was to lie on your back in the water, close your eyes, hold your nose and breathe through a hollow piece of bamboo stick.

If Daniel Boone could do it when hiding from blood-thirsty Indians, then so could we. Thinking back on it now it was all a bit point-less because "Who were we hiding from anyway?" and secondly if you were a marauding blood thirsty Indian, you couldn't really miss us ly-ing in twelve inches of water! That said it was pretty difficult to do and there had to be a huge amount of trust in your friends.

You had to be sure that they weren't going to block your air with their hands, or worse still stand on your stomach as you lay there like a corpse under the water. I remember trying it a few times but my nerves were gone waiting for the messing to start. I would lie there waiting for some one to bang down on the bamboo, breaking my teeth and ripping the gums in the process. Oh Yes, really funny, not to mention swallowing a gallon of the stinking water at the same time.

Summer Days at McGuirk's River

When playing with water, dams, and rafts the hours passed by really quickly and when dinner was ready back in Turnapin we always got the call from my mother. Ma would just stand at our back door and do a Tarzan like call through cupped hands to her mouth,

"GERRRRRRRRRAAAAAAAAARRRRRRRRRRRRDDDDDD"

Although we were roughly a quarter of a mile away, we could hear her wafting through on the summer breeze. What a pair of lungs that woman had. Within seconds Noel and I would be gone. Running up the road like the cartoon character "the Roadrunner". Meep! Meep!, past Curran's (pronounced KUR-RAN-SIZZ) turning in at Heeney's gap and up into our yard in 5 minutes flat. Quick wash of the hands at the outside tap, then straight into the kitchen table, elbows out, ears back, and starving with the hunger. Those dinners got some deaths.

On a few occasions rather than taking the long trek home for dinner which interrupted our sea faring endeavours, we brought along a picnic to have our food "alfresco". This involved stuffing plates, cutlery, bread, butter, brown sauce, and salt into a small suit case and carrying it down with us. The Maddens supplied the pan, the teapot and the fresh eggs and then the job was "oxo". The eggs were supplied by Dolly Madden's hens and she did great business selling eggs to the people in Turnapin who didn't have hens themselves. Many a time my mother would say "Gerard, you wouldn't slip down to Dolly for a few eggs for me, would you, there's a good chap," and yes I always went.

When I knocked on her door for eggs she generally had to gather them there and then from underneath the hens. The hen house was way down at the end of her garden and wearing boots and a floral pinny we would both saunter down to the hen house together to get the eggs.

Chapter 4

She wrapped each egg separately in newspaper just like a big sweet. At the back of Dolly's hen house there was a gap through the ditch into Joe Harris's yard where all the old C.I.E. buses went to die. This bus graveyard was another world of adventure for us. In the hulks of these buses there were "birds nests" to be found and later when the Hino trucks came, small wooden crates could be got there which were ideal for trolley cabs. I have a vague memory of being in this yard with a young Jimmy "Skitcher" Heeney and him falling from a rope tied to a bus lying on it's side. Whether he had an illness at that stage already, I don't know, but he never really recovered his health after this and died in early 1972 aged just 16. His mother Chris, died later the same year, they say of a broken heart.

Dolly Madden, was a tallish, thin, gentle woman who smoked like a trooper. As she wrapped the egg, she spoke softly, still managing to hold her "Woodbine" cigarette in the corner of her mouth as she did so. Sometimes there would be an ash nearly an inch long on the cigarette, but it still managed to hang on. When picnic time came and we needed to cook a bit of food the first thing we needed was a fire. Gerry Madden was the man for the matches, because he smoked as well, just like his mother Dolly.

Summer Days at McGuirk's River

Very close to McGuirk's river, on a corner where four fields met we created a "Den" in among all the blackberry bushes. We made a pathway through one of the ditches into the center and we created this type of cave. We called it the "Man from Uncle" den. There was a 1960s Television series called " The Man from U.N.C.L.E." with two special agents called Napoleon Solo and Illya Kuryakin.

This was our biggest den and was headquarters for all of our local missions when we were armed with our UNCLE kits containing guns (water pistols), torches, invisible ink pens and false identities. We usually bought these kits either in Kitty's in Beaumount or the Hostess in Larkhill. Homemade "weapons" like slings, bows and arrows were also stored there as well.

For some crazy reason we once decided that our outdoor picnic would take place inside the den. Yes, we actually lit the fire inside. Maybe it was raining outside, but it was to prove to be a disaster not even budding spies could sort out. The stones to enclose the fire were gathered and laid out in a circle on the floor of the den. Newspapers were torn up and sticks placed on top. The match was struck, paper lit and pretty much immediately the place started to fill with smoke.

Chapter 4

Undaunted we figured let the fire burn for few minutes and the smoke would die down. The frying pan was put in place over the flames so we decided to fry the eggs in relays. Running in and out, catching our breath, from under our air filled jumpers, oh yes, those eggs were ours! Through all the coughing, we ran black faced and bleary eyed in and out through-out the three minutes it took to fry the eggs. Finally they were done and we lifted them of the pan with tears streaming down our cheeks.

Slapped onto buttered batch bread, with egg yoke dripping, then covered with salt and "Chef" brown sauce, you just could not taste better. "What about your dirty hands?" I hear you ask, "Hands, What hands?" no hands used, we ate the sambo's with our elbows. Did I mention the flies? Oh yes, there was millions of them, probably the same ones that lived in the nearby cowpats. Thankfully the thick smoke did have one benefit and even the flies got lost and died in it.

As we ate our sambos we looked on at the blaze within and eventually the whole den went up. The smoke plume could be seen from far and near, but thankfully by the following year it had all grown back again.

CHAPTER 5

Birthday Party in Hillfarm House

Back in the sixties we had our very own "Girls Aloud" living in Turnapin Lane and these were Margaret Farrell, Denise Farrell, Chris Boland, Marie Moore, Jean & Lena Darcy, Marie McCormack and Joan & Frances Donohue. These were the glamour-pussed, mini-skirted girls of the swinging 60s who were living amongst us in a Turnapin that had changed little since the end of the 2nd World War. Up until 1967 we operated with outside dry toilets beside the coal houses, cooking-ranges and water from the lion headed waterpumps which stood on the terrace between no 3 and 4 Roberts/Smiths and no13 and 14 Peppers/Carrolls.

Birthday Party in Hillfarm House

Girls Aloud plus 1, C. Boland, J. Joyce, M. Joyce, M. Farrell, L. Darcy

These girls were all in their late teens or early twenties and they could be seen every Saturday evening, running from house to house getting ready to go out, their faces caked with pan stick (the very original fake tan), hair netted in the rollers, all getting dolled upto go off to the 'Palm Beach' in Portmarnock or the 'Pavillion' in Rush to dance to the Irish showbands. The local "lads" at that time were Tommy Carolan, Michael "Skobie" Moore, Jim, Joey and Mick Darcy, John and David Wilson, Tommy, Jimmy and Anthony Roberts, Matt and Jerry Heeney, David and Charles "Gaggo" Pepper, Bobby, Pat, Mick, and Kevin Donohue and of course who could forget the one and only Seamus "Doc" Roche. This generation were spared the scourge of emigration with nearly full employment in the booming Ireland of the mid 1960s.

Chapter 5

Local factories like Lilmar, Plessey, Bush, Palm Grove and Brother were buzzing and one of these "factory" girls was my young aunt Chris Boland. She had a small grey two tone record player and I would listen to her records on it during my visits into my Granny Boland's house in no 33 Turnapin Lane. Chris was and still is a very pragmatic person, so in return for access to the music I had to do some housework. She would get me to polish and shine the tiled and lino-ed floors in 33. This was done on my hands and knees with a rolled up jumper as the shining cloth. I especially remember the yellow and green tiles in the hall which were always freezing even in summertime.

Records by the Seekers like "The Carnival is over" and "Hey there Georgy Girl", along with Mary Hopkin's "Those were the Days" were the soundtrack for my hours of floor sweeping and shining.

Birthday Party in Hillfarm House

Sean Dunphy's "If I could Choose" was in there as well and I seem to remember the "B" side was a song with the words "And her hair hung down, hung'a down her back and my heart went tick, tick a tick a tack, like Charlie's Joe's , Jimmy John and Jack's, my heart went tick, tick a tick a tack". Despite that I can't remember the title!

At that time No 33 was very quiet compared to my own house in No 21, as my Granny Boland would have been in hospital. I remember one afternoon I was polishing there amongst Chris and her pals, all "nesting" around a coal fire in the sitting room and having a good "Gosster" (Gossip). I was put outside the sitting room door but I still heard one of them whispering, "Did you hear, that you know who, is having a B-A-B-Y, spelling out the last word, so I wouldn't understand. I just popped my head back in the door and shouted "Baby!" They were stunned into silence and then they all burst out laughing. No more of that gossip, especially with me around.

From time to time my two married Boland aunts, Patty and Breda, would come here on visits with their children, especially during the summertime. Patty had two sons Jimmy and Gary, and one daughter called Florence. Breda, had two sons Hubert and Glenn, and two daughters Carmel and Sharon. These mixed well with the locals and their Turnapin cousins. As a matter of fact, Florence O'Neill later married John Connolly from no 25 in Turnapin.

I don't have a lot of memories of my Granny Boland, all I have are brief shadows and glimpses. She moved slowly and wore a dark flowery pinny. She died in Sept 1968, when I was just ten after having a stroke a year earlier. The only clear memory I have of her is being carried from a bedroom to the sitting room in no 33, by my mother and my aunt Breda.

Chapter 5

Frances Donohue was one of this gaggle of girls and she had a younger sister called Phyllis. The big party in question was for her.

I am thinking this was her 10th or 11th birthday. There was great excitement because birthday parties were very few and far between back then. The party was going to be held in Phyllis's home, called Hillfarm House which was on a corner just down from the top of Turnapin Lane. The Birthday girl, Phyllis was the 2nd youngest of 16 children. Jack Donohue had been a buyer for Haffners, the Dublin pork butchers and had set up on his own. He moved to Hillfarm in the early 1950's and on this small 10 acre farm he bred pigs for his own family business. The previous owners of Hillfarm were the Lynn family, who originally came from Crossmolina in County Mayo. Michael Lynn one of the sons was involved in the building of a few houses around the area with his brother P.J. Lynn. One of these being "Lismoy" at the top of Coolock Lane, now demolished, with a new Centra Shop now on the site.

At one stage Mr. Donohue had three pork butcher shops on the go in Dublin. One shop was in Drumcondra, the other was in Moore Street and the third one was in Cabra and they were considered prosperous. All of the family were involved and Frances worked in the Moore street shop. She was great fun and I really liked her.

Frances and Chris took control of the party, especially the music. At the appointed time, most of the kids from the Lane assembled up at Dunne's corner. We all had our card and little present in our hands. Chris shouted "Boys on the path at Flood's side, and girls on the path on Dunne's side". We were in disbelief at this carry on. I was nine, maybe ten tops and girls were just not on the radar, absolutely no way. I remember Johnny Darcy was a complete messer and there

Birthday Party in Hillfarm House

Above : My Grandparents Christina and Jack Boland
Below: Phyllis Donohue in the family shop in Moore street

was no way we would be walking down the back road to Hillfarm in pairs linking anybody, least of all girls. When we all got down to the house, which was a modest two storey old farmhouse, we were all herded through the porch which was at the near gable end, on through into a big square room with chairs along the walls. There was a small room, off the square room, maybe the kitchen which had black and white tiles. Some of us hung back and left the room and made our way around to the pig sheds to investigate. A few hundred pigs are very noisy and smelly. I remember being warned by Chris not to go around near the Pigs, but we were all giddy and just ran away.

The meat curing shed or smoking shed as it was known was another major attraction and this stood opposite the house on the right as you entered the yard. Eventually Frances emerged from the house screaming and shouting at us, so with the help of one or two of her brothers, Pat, Kevin, Mick or Robert we were tracked down and returned to the party room for the big 'Happy Birthday' song. At this stage, Chris and Frances were totally stressed out and rapidly losing interest. Phyllis's mother Mary was there, sitting on one of the chairs watching it all unfold. She always looked Italian to me. Brian, Phyllis's younger brother, was not impressed with the carry on during the singing of the Happy Birthday song. Phyllis was a lovely quite girl. She was wearing a red jacket and a ribbon in her blonde hair. She was one or two years older than me, but as we got older she didn't really mix with us that much.

Jimmy Pepper from no 10 in Turnapin, did a bit of driving for Jack Donohue so the older Pepper children, Brian, Stephen and Stephenie, mixed more with Brian and Phyllis. Meanwhile back at the party, things were about to go downhill. Chris and Frances decided that the room needed atmosphere, so the curtains were drawn and the party

Birthday Party in Hillfarm House

room was plunged into darkness. I am opting for the "Hucklebuck" by Brendan Boyer as the first song on after the cake, with Frances and Chris giving us the demo. It could have been the twist by Chubby Checker, but there was definitely a twist going on. "Up and down, and round and round we go again, baby let me know you love me so, Come on let's twist again." At least twenty of us there, some dancing, (the girls) and then the boys who were mostly chasing after each other, pushing and tripping each other up. Johnny Darcy crouched and hid underneath the table that the record player was on and from that vantage point he was looking up at the girls knickers as they spun around. I have to confess I was with him, along with a few others. When we were spotted by the girls, they made a bit of a meal of it, running about and squealing the place down.

Chapter 5

Lights on immediately, music stopped, big scatter, Chris and Frances were losing it big time. Then lights off again and wait for it, the "slow" set. We had been matched up at the top of the road before we came down but I had run away. So me being "single" if you like I was matched up with the birthday girl herself. I was pushed into slow set with Phyllis, the rest of the lads were now taking part but really hamming it up. "Silence is Golden" by the Tremeloes is a vague memory as we lurched from side to side holding hands. Phyllis was blushing and so was I, both of us thinking, "Jesus make this song end quickly."

Post Script : After this particular party there was one in my house for me for my birthday. There was the usual big Turnapin gang there including Phyllis. I was playing up, showing off, so my mother duly slapped me in front of everyone. I remember nothing else from that party! it's called TMB (Traumatic Mental Block). I never had another Birthday party in 21 Turnapin Lane. "I had my chance" as my mother said "and you blew it!"

CHAPTER 6

Q Bikes come to Turnapin

While growing up in Turnapin, bicycles were always an absolute necessity and everybody had at least one. You must remember that our small enclave of 36 cottages were miles away from anywhere. Our schools and shops in Santry were a full mile away but at least for these you had the option of a bus. If, however, you were heading to Clonshaugh, Belcamp, or Northside Shopping Centre, down along the back-road, it was Shank's mare (walking) or the bicycle. These bicycles were very functional and were the big old ones with the coil sprung saddles and any colour you wanted as long as it was black!

Q Bikes come to Turnapin

As a young boy when I was sick in bed, the routine was a big glass bottle of Lucozade with the yellow cellophane wrapper, along with heavy doses' of the gross yellow foul tasting medicine that seemed to be the same whatever your illness was. These bouts of illness usually only lasted three or four days and by the 3rd day you would be starting to get on Ma's nerves a bit, jumping in and out of the bed and generally starting to mess a bit with the younger ones. Ma would eventually crack and declare "I don't F'in' care, you can shite blue rags, your going up that road to school in the mornin'!"

One treat for me as a little sick boy was getting comics like the "Beano," "Dandy," or the "Topper" to read while I was laid up in the bed. Ma always spoilt me a bit when I was sick because I was her little helper. I was the eldest and I did all the big jobs for her when she needed me.

One of my jobs was to meet her off the bus from the bus corner to carry down the shopping with her when she came back from Power's Supermarket in Talbot Street. She would take one side of the bag and I would take the other, oh yes, back then I was her little "Topper."

Chapter 6

Another job for me was to go to the Launderette when the drying for clothes got bad, especially in the wintertime. This was a big one- because I usually went on my own and it took me all of a Saturday morning to do it. I was sent in on the 41 bus, with pillow cases full of clothes to the Launderette just past Binn's Bridge, on the corner of Belvedere Road. All the machines in there worked on an English or Irish two shilling piece and it was always lovely and warm. The smell of detergent powder as hot water mixes with it, brings me back to this scene, instantly. Ma always warned me to stay inside while I was there but in between loading, washing and drying I did a bit of scouting around outside. There was Smith's cake shop on the corner where I would buy a cream slice and a bottle of milk. Never to miss an opportunity to get a bit of shopping in, Ma would give a little list to get her a few messages while I was there. Brady's butchers next door to the Washerette for the meat and across the road, where Black Tie is now there was a fish shop. Bradys and the Washerette, now called Supreme Wash, are still there today over 40 years later.

Q Bikes come to Turnapin

Da usually bought the comics in the Hostess or Kings' up in Santry. They were always printed in lovely vivid colours and were a brilliant distraction for me as I recovered. With my vivid imagination I found myself daydreaming about adventures in all sorts of places from the cosy comfort of my bed.

When any of us were sick we got promoted to the parents big double bed for during the day at least and this was absolute comfort. Having a whole bed all to yourself was heaven and if you were really bad, the television would be dragged in to keep you company. I much preferred the comics and little Billy Whizz was a favourite character of mine, speeding around from here to there, with his quiffed hair and spinning legs. Pete's Pockets was another one, all about a boy who faced all sorts of danger and had the solution to every problem deep down in his pockets. He could be the fore-runner of McEyver if you like.

BILLY WHIZZ

During one bout of sickness it was the Q bikes that really struck a chord with me. These were Beano characters and together these bunch of kids managed to sort out all sorts of villians while cycling around on these special bicycles wearing helmets with radios built into them. When I got better I was determined that myself and my buddies were going to have our very own bike gang, going places and having all sorts of adventures together. I showed them a few of the Q Bikes stories in the Beano and everyone got as excited as me about the whole thing. Johnny Masters was the leader of the Q Bikes and everybody wanted to be him.

Chapter 6

The problem for us however, was that our bikes looked nothing like theirs. The Raleigh Chopper had yet to hit Ireland, so what we had to do was make up bikes of our own. I suppose you would call it customizing, but it was actually much bigger than that, because we had to built them up from scratch. The first problem we had was that we had no money, or very little at least. The next thing we needed of course were parts like frames, wheels, chains, etc and plenty of them.

I am not sure who stumbled on the Aladdin's cave first but for some reason in the late 1960's, people would travel along our back road and dump bikes into the big ditches that ran along the end of our gardens. These deep ditches ran for miles along the backroad leading on down to Jolly's Hill passing McKennas' big house and out on to Clonshaugh. Typically they were the big old black type with Hercules and Raleigh being the name badges I remember seeing the most. We called them "High Nellies" and they were very old fashioned and usually only ridden by old people. We would snigger at them passing along the road shouting after them "Hey there Granny grunt, give us a go on your high nellie!"

High Nellie bike

Q Bikes come to Turnapin

They just didn't fit in with the new modern era that was the swinging 60's. Now and then a teenager's black bicycle with the smaller frame and wheels would turn up and these were the ones we were after. The very odd time a racing bike would turn up, maybe stolen somewhere and just dumped, but this was very rare and I never managed to strike gold and find one.

Chapter 6

It was always a good start if you came across one with two wheels with neither tyre punctured. As we walked along the ditches looking for discarded bicycles we quickly developed scouting skills like the Indians in the cowboys films we saw on television. If the long grasses or the tall "Devil's spit" weeds on the banks of the ditches were trampled flat you knew that someone had dragged up a bicycle, or sometimes an old pram and pushed it over the bank into the ditch.

We always had ropes with us and nobody liked getting down into the deep dark, wet and smelly ditch to tie it on to a find. Usually the person who did this bit had first claim on the bicycle or any part that they needed. I suppose it was a little bit like salvage on a wreck found out at sea. Ladies bicycles were regarded as "bad" finds and only good for individual parts. These were disassembled there and then on the roadside bank with their "Sissy" frames and mud-flaps unceremoniusly returned to their watery graves at the bottom of the ditches.

Pages of Garda Review stating importance of Raleigh bikes to the Force

Q Bikes come to Turnapin

During this "Q Bikes" summer fad, the race was on to get the best lookalike Q bike. Lads with smaller brothers were lumbered because you had to make their bikes as well and it had to look as good as yours and this was harder than you think. First of all, your bike was usually finished first and once it was finished all you wanted to do was jump up on it and ride away to show it off. Of course your bike got the best parts, like the best chromed wheels and handlebars. If you left the brother's bike unfinished, he was chasing you to finish it, running in crying to the Ma that he had no bike, so, as far as possible it was best to do all at the same time.

This particular summer the whole road was in on the act. The whole road of the boys only, I must add, as the girls were busy skipping, hopscotching and playing mammies and nurses. Jimmy "Skitcher" Heeney, myself and the brother Noel, Hacker (Noel) Murphy, Johnny Darcy, John Connolly, Derek and Gerry Madden. The sprats were Paulie and Willie Heeney, David Cooley, Paul Darcy, Paul and Dessie Murphy. It conicided with us starting to weed bulkyshanks for Willie Snow and Stephen Fowler. This was crucial because we needed cash to spruce the bikes up with back carriers, mirrors, flags, stands, horns, streamers, chrome tape, dynamo lights, new tubes and tyres. There was a shop in Dorset Street, a straight run in on the bus, that supplied all you needed to support your bicycle "habit". I remember it had baskets with all sorts of stuff outside the door. Once you passed over Binns Bridge you were nearly there. It was on the left hand side close to where McCormacks' bicycle shop is now.

Some lads were better than others with mechanical parts. I was reasonable enough and we all worked in our own backyards. Some had big brothers to help them. Johnny Darcy had Joey, Mick and Jim while Noel Murphy had Liam "Foreigner" Murphy, his older brother.

Chapter 6

Noel's father, Bill Murphy was a great man to fix a buckled bicycle wheel. He once worked in a Mongey's bicycle shop in Swords and he was highly regarded as a man to "spoke" the old sportscar wheels. Bill's nickname was "Hacksaw," hence Noel his son was called "Hacker". Once I was in Murphy's back yard doing some bicycle tinkering and their unfortunate dog "Butch" Murphy, had been poisoned. I looked around to see Mr Murphy, swinging the poor ould dog by the back legs, around and around, to make the dog sick and throw up the offending poisoned food.

Bill 'Hacksaw' Murphy with Butch his dog

Q Bikes come to Turnapin

Himself and Mr Darcy had decided to give poor Butch a few swigs of Whiskey to make him vomit. Murphy's nextdoor neighbour in no 31, Mrs Redmond, also known as "Gocky Pooch-cher" was chief suspect with regard to the poison. She got blamed for everything. As he was spinning the unfortunate dog around he had his trade mark cigarette butt puckered up in his lips. Did the dog survive? No I don't think he did, but I am sure one of the Murphy's could tell us his fate. Dogs around Turnapin always got the family surname. There was Butch Murphy, Coalie Carley, Rusty Mahony, Rex Heeney, Tiger Heeney, Prince Caul, Rory Cooley and Brandy Donohue. Dunne's had a dog, who was just known as "Dunne's Dog" and I remember him croaking it in Geraghty's field after he had been poisoned.

Back with the bicycles and me being the eldest, I had no older brother to help me. I, however, had an ace in the hole because my youngest uncle Joseph was a great mechanic. He was always in our yard fixing something or other and whistling as he went it. He had a lovely soft whistle, which he generated through his tongue and teeth, he also had a really dry sense of humour. He wore a soft cap which made him look older than he was, but most importantly for us, he could put anything mechanical together.

Chains were especially difficult, especially when taking off the split link-clip. When removing links making the chains smaller, special punchs were required and Joseph was your only man. To be fair he helped everyone with their chains because this was a very tricky job. As important as his mechanical skills were, however, he also had rows of shelves full of nuts and bolts, boxes of spanners and wrenchs, all in the big shed in our yard. If we ever needed anything we always headed to the big shed. This shed had a block and tackle with one or two bench vices, and was built by Da's friend, Vinny Pepper who lived

Chapter 6

across the road in No 13. His eldest daughter Veronica, or "Pepsi" as she was also known by, was a childhood sweetheart of mine. She was my very first proper date when we went to the "Flicks" together and I can still remember that her pink trouser suit matched her pink lipstick. The film was the "Go Between" with Alan Bates and it had a few heavy scenes in it that mortified the both of us.

Joseph Cooley at Dunnes' corner

With Joseph on our team our bicycles were always the best mechanically. I make this distinction because it wasn't really all about how they worked, but more importantly it was how they looked. For a start they couldn't be black. The colour you re-painted the frame and mudguards really depended on what colour your gates or sheds had been painted recently and so we used the half empty cans still lying around. When you re-opened the cans of "gloss finish" it usually had a skin of dried paint lying over the wet paint below. The trick was to take this skin out wholesale because if it broke up, the bits would appear in the paint coat. The heap of cinders, spud skins and tea leaves lying under the hedge, or beside the coal house was a good spot

99

for the dripping skin of paint. To let the paint drip on the concrete, was absolutely, a severe thumping offence. The paint would be pretty thick and in the really early days, water was added to thin it out, but this reduced the paint to unusable big blobs. Joseph once suggested a small drop of petrol instead of the water which worked a treat and of course soft clean dry paint brushes were always in demand.

This particular summer there was red and yellow paint knocking around our yard and Noel got some silver paint from his buddy John Connolly "Clonlure the long hoor" who lived in No 25 beside Roches. There was a young lad named Michael Roche who appeared every now and again, and for at least one of our summers he was

in the Turnapin Gang. He was a friendly sort with a nice smile and a head of flaming red hair. I am happy to report I met up with him a few years ago and he was still the same as ever. After all these years he still remembered his adventures with us in Turnapin. Back with the silver paint, Tom Connolly, John's father, was a country man and was great for painting his front gates and railings silver. The hedge leaves would also be painted sil-

Michael Roche   ver, which looked a little bit like frost, but in time they grew out and the next cut would remove them. I don't think anyone in Turnapin ever used undercoat, so the drying time between coats, depending on the weather, was at least a week!

Before you started painting anything, the frame was stripped bare of all parts and laid upside down standing on the handle bars and saddle. Brakes, pedals, and saddles were generally left on because they were really too difficult or too fiddly to get off. Cardboard was placed under the handle bars so the chrome wasn't scratched. The back wheel was always the last to come off, because pedaling an up-turned bicycle wheel had a sort of mesmerising effect on you. The wheel would be spinning really fast and someone was always tempted to plunge a stick or finger into the spinning spokes. There was also the dare to stop the spinning back wheel by placing your open hand on the rubber tyre. Jerry Heeney was a good man at this one. He was much older than us and he was a "man." He drove a motor bike and worked in Jones, so his hands were rough and the spinning tyre didn't burn him.

I started on my mudguards first, painting them red while Noel started on his with the silver. There was a slight problem in so far as we only had one paint brush, so he had to wait for me to finish my pieces, so his mudguards had a bit of red in the silver, at least at the start. The back reflector on the rear mudguard was always taken off before the painting started. When painting the frame and because it was lying upside down, you were missing the top sides of the frame, so at some stage the frame had to be lifted up and stood upright. This was very tricky. The frame was now covered in paint and this is usually where it all went wrong. As I turned my frame over, the wet painted front forks, spun and turned, hitting my legs and trousers. As I grabbed the handlebars the paint had started to spread onto the chrome. When I got it upright I noticed that the paint was running. I needed to paint it out, but Noel had the only brush and was using a different colour. In the end I used my fingers to rub the paint in.

Then "Boy", our family dog got in on the act and was jumping in on top us, licking our hands and looking for pets. He brushed off the wet paint leaving his hairs on everything. Oh yes, painting was never easy. I managed it but Noel was a disaster painting his, so I usually took over his stuff. We had a few tricks of the trade when putting all the parts together. Clothes pegs were used to center the wheels when tightening them into the frames. If there was a bit of rust on the chrome, a bit of wet cigarette silver paper rubbed on it would make it disappear.

After a week, both our bicycles were finished and ready for the "Q Bike" parade on the Saturday morning. They looked brilliant. Coloured plastic streamers coming out of the handlebar grips, mirrors and horns, Me and Noel were really chuffed. Da had got us a few "PUT A TIGER IN YOUR TANK" stickers from the ESSO station down the road and we stuck them on the crossbars.

All through this week the evening get togethers had been full of talk about what you were doing, colours, accessories etc. It was really exciting. I had shown uncle Joseph a picture of the Q Bikes in the comic and late in the week, he called me down to the shed, swore me to secrecy, insisting I closed my eyes and put my hands out. Opening my eyes I was now holding a blue motor bike helmet. Wow! I was made up, I was going to be Johnny Masters, the leader. Joseph told me not to tell Noel where I got it, or he would be in big trouble with him. Noel was Josephs' mechanic buddy and he helped him get engines in and out of the cars and trucks. There and then I ran and hid the helmet in the cab of one the many old wrecks of lorries that were lying around our yard. It was the Friday before the big meet the next morning up at Dunne's corner. Rumours were flying around about a "Walkie-Talkie" set sent home by Johnny Darcy's relations in England, someone else was spoofing that their bike even had an engine, but I kept my powder dry.

I was really excited and got up early. I had taken the helmet out of the cab and I put it under my bed. The Parade was to be at around eleven o'clock. I was watching the gang gathering up at Dunne's corner from my house at the bottom of the road. In the distance the bikes were gleaming in early morning sunshine and I was getting nervous. Some bicycles were on their own stands and some were standing up against the kerb using the pedal to anchor them in place.

Dunne's corner

Q Bikes come to Turnapin

There was a lot of running and jumping but no one was cycling around. John Connolly waited on us, while the two Maddens, Gerry and Derek, came up through Heeney's gap, through our yard and up with us to the corner. It was time. Putting the helmet on slowly, I strapped it in place and let the rest cycle on ahead. Noel's bike looked great, better than mine in fact, the all silver paint really looked the part. My colours, yellow and red looked a bit rough, but the helmet would swing it for me. On we went up the road, passing the fountain outside Peppers and then on up to the corner. All the bikes looked well, but as expected the blue helmet stole the show. Johnny Darcy was jealous, I knew by him. No talk of leaders yet I didn't want to push it.

With all of us assembled we really needed to show everybody our all our hard work. As the "Q Bike" gang started to gather one by one, the excitement had really started to rise. Along with the owners, we also had the sprats running from bike to bike looking for a "go" or a "carry". Some of the sprats were so small that they had to peddle the bikes riding it under the cross bar sideways. This was very dangerous and very uncomfortable but it was better than shining the saddle with the cheeks of their arses as their small legs were stretched to tip toes on the pedals. Then someone made the call to go, honking horns as hard as they could. We all raced to our standing bicycles and on we jumped. To see eight "new" bicycles, all leaving together was really a sight to behold. We looked just like the "Q bikes" in the Beano comic. Our first trip was to the back road to Gerry Madden's house because he had a slow puncture and he needed his pump. So we all headed off together with a few sprats already on the cross bars and sitting on the back carriers. As we turned at Donohue's corner we cycled in full formation and there was a great sense of joy everywhere.

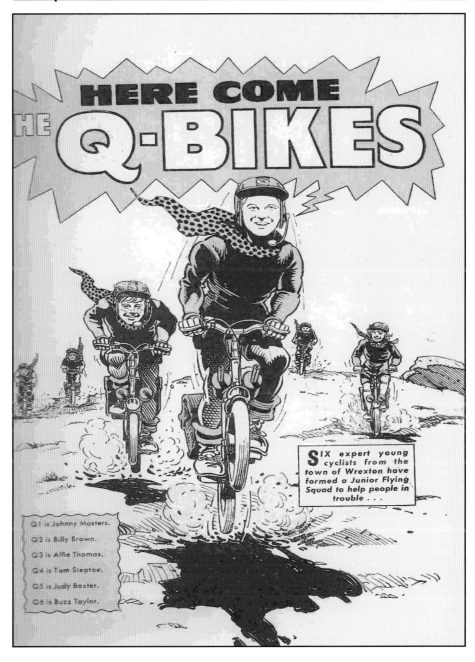

Curran's gate and cottage on the back road. Tree on right is at Tinker's corner.

Chapter 6

McKenna's field was on the right just past McDermott's cart road and it was a golden yellow sea of wheat. As we passed Curran's gate heading on to Maddens, we met Jerry Heeney on his wine coloured Yamaha motor bike. He waved us down to tell us that two, Tinker's horsedrawn caravans were just pulling in at Tinker's Corner, which was just past Madden's house.

Johnny Darcy was dispatched to do a recky and after two minutes there was a squawking noise behind me. I heard some words sounding like a radio broadcast saying "Hello, Johnny here, can you hear me?" Noel Muphy had something to his mouth and he was saying into it "Hello Johnny, Hacker here over, got you loud and clear."

I couldn't believe my eyes or ears, they had Man from U.N.C.L.E Walkie-Talkies sets and Jesus, they were brilliant. Johnny answered excitedly "Heres' the Tinkers! Over, Heres' the Tinkers! Over" and so our very first Q Bike adventure started.

CHAPTER 7

Santry Woods, Rafts and Bulrushes.

My father was the very first person ever to bring me to Santry Woods. I was a very young child and it was Autumn and we were up picking hazel nuts and walnuts before Halloween. Da was a great man to crack hazel-nuts with his teeth and he knew the "Wood," as he calls it, inside out because, just like me, he had grown up in Turnapin lane and he had spent so much time there as a child himself. We would pick the nuts and then he would place them in a pillow case underneath the bottom shelf in our hot-press to ripen with the help of the darkness and heat.

Santry Woods, Rafts and Bulrushes.

This was the infamous hot-press that was situated in the corner of our small front sitting room. It had a hot water cylinder in the lower half and this hot press was a dis-functional nightmare. It had doors at ground level that would only open six inches because the couch was in the way. The doors were always breaking at the hinges and made of plywood that often splintered and stuck into enquiring hands and arms. It was a home-made job and probably built by my uncle Dominic Duffy who was handy with plumbing and wood. The bag of nuts would be placed down in the bottom, right at the back.

As we got older, the Turnapin crew would sometimes make trips up to Santry Woods. It wasn't very far and we would cut through Geraghty's field and go down along the river at the far end of the field. From here we could walk underneath the main road through the bridge under the road and step out in the Woods with the little old red cottage to our right. This is where Jack Roberts used to live. After that we walked a further 50 feet over to the edge of the lake. This route guaranteed us wet feet, especially if we weren't wearing the wellies.

If you were in short trousers however, which most of us were, these boots would cut the legs off you just behind your calves. To ease this "pain" you had to fold the boots down to stop them rubbing on the bare skin. This made them shorter, so you had to remember your wellie boot height as you walked in the gushing river water, otherwise disaster would strike. Not only would you have wet feet but you would stink of stagnant water as well.

Santry Woods was a huge expanse to us and it was always dark because of the dense tree cover there, especially during the summertime. It was really and truly a wilderness, exactly what budding Tom Sawyers and Huckleberry Finns like ourselves wanted.

Chapter 7

We were always told stories of Lady Margaret Domvile, wife of Sir Charles Domvile, sailing around the lake between the islands on a steam driven pleasure boat, which fired our imaginations no end. The mansion that once stood there was Santry Court and it had a tree lined walk which led down to the lake. With the mansion long gone the estate went into dereliction and in our time the lake had long become a swamp and the two islands previously surrounded by water had long since become just part of this stinking stagnant swamp. Up stream from this swamp there was an old stone bridge and we used to get under it to scream as loud as we could because there was a great echo there. On this particular visit we didn't venture up that far, we had other things on our minds.

Rear view of Santry Court, burnt in 1941, and demolished in 1959

Santry Woods, Rafts and Bulrushes.

This particular Summer with the help of a lot of rain bearing thunder storms, the water levels rose significantly and the islands magically became islands again. We spotted this when we were coming home from Larkhill School on the bus. This presented us with the challenge of building a raft that would actually float and bring us to the "lost" islands of Santry Woods. What we were going to do when we got there, wasn't really the point, we just had to get there and get there by raft.

I was about ten or eleven at the time and it was the usual Turnapin crew of Noel Murphy, Johnny Darcy, Noel Cooley and myself. Derek and Gerry Madden were drafted in with us because all our "sailing" and raft building skills would have been gotten down at McGuirk's River which was in front of their house around on the back road. Derek Madden was good with putting things together. Once he cut a big council tar barrel right down the middle using a hack-saw and we tried to float it on McGuirk's River but it sank within thirty seconds of going into the water. The many ghosts of past "floating" failures were going to be laid to rest on this expedition.

After watching an episode of Tom Sawyer called the "Pirate's Lair," where Tom had used some small barrels as floats under a raft, I had decided that a few small oil drums were the answer for us. Tom was trying to get to Smuggler's Cove, avoiding shipwrecks that reached out from the murky depths to pull him and Huckleberry to a watery grave. Old oil drums would save us and there were lots of these to be found in our big shed back in our yard. This shed was where uncle Joseph, the mechanic in the family, did most of his work. Engine oil was always being replaced so there were always a few empty five gallon Castrol oil drums knocking around.

113

Santry Woods, Rafts and Bulrushes.

Noel and me had a look around the big shed and pulled out the four drums that were required. There was a 4 pram-wheeled trolley lying around from the previous years "Stock Car" fad so we put the drums into that. It was painted a bright red and it had a big no 6 painted on the back and it was just about big enough for the 4 drums to fit snug and tight for the journey south to the Woods.

I remember one of the drums was nearly full so we just brought it around to the back of the shed and dumped the oil out onto the ground. We were in a hurry and the oil seemed to flow forever. It "glopped, glopped" slowly as it poured slowly out through the extended plastic nozzle. To this day when I top up my car with oil, that "glopping" noise as it flows into the engine brings me right back to this incident. I am not sure whose idea the emptying out of the oil drum was, but it was a bad one. Even when I was watching the oil spread out and soak into the coal and slack covered mud, I knew it was wrong. It was nearly a full five gallon drum of unused engine oil and it certainly took the good out of the day for us, because both of us got into big trouble over it when we surfaced later on that evening tired and weary from our day's adventure in Santry Woods.

Da and uncle Joesph were not impressed but when Grandad Cooley found out about it the next day, he was really disgusted with us. Both me and Noel took our punishment quietly and when the stinging on our legs had finally died down we were made cover the oil patch over with dry filling which thankfully soaked most of it up. I remember asking Grandad how much the oil was and I even offered to pay for the oil we had destroyed. It didn't help at all because Grandad didn't really care about money, I think he was just disgusted that we would just emptied it out deliberately on the ground and just wasted it. We had let him down and I was digusted that we had done it.

Chapter 7

On our reconnaissance mission to the Woods a few days previous, we had noticed there was already a few pallets floating in the water, abandoned relics of previous failed attempts to get a raft out onto the water. We decided that we would use the best and biggest of these, so we only had to get the oil drums there, along with some twine to lash them to the wood. Noel Murphy had a brainwave involving nails, which would be driven through the wood into the barrels below to help fix them in place. Seemed like a good idea at the time, so we went with it instead of the twine. Armed with a hammer, six inch nails, and our trusty bright Red "No 6" trolley carrying the four drums, the "Raft" gang headed off to Santry Woods. Gerry Madden had a penknife and he always brought matches. Camp fires were seldom really needed but they were lit anyway. Fires lit out in the Jungle were always exciting.

We had to go by road because of the trolley. Up at the bus corner we crossed over at Casey's, but while we ran, with myself pulling the trolley and nobody holding the four drums in place, I hit the kerb and they all scattered and rolled out into the road. What a din there was. The horns of the speeding cars blared, as we tried to retrieve the rolling drums from the path of oncoming cars and trucks. Everybody in our little group was blaming everybody else. One or two of the Cooley and Murphy sprats burst into tears and ran home there and then because of all the commotion. We re-grouped at Casey's, with a little blond Joseph Casey looking on over his small front wall, bemused by the whole noisy carry-on. His mother, "Vann" Casey came out, waved a disapproving cigarette in our direction, gathered him up and took him inside. I spotted Lizzie Hynes who had just got off the bus, standing watching the whole thing. It wouldn't be long before the word of our carry on up at the bus corner would be all over the terrace. Tele-phone, Tele-gram, Tele-Lizzie!

Santry Woods, Rafts and Bulrushes.

With someone now holding the drums in place I pulled the trolley along past the little cottage where the McDonald sisters lived. At this time Betty and Maura lived there with their mother Molly and they were always pottering about in their garden.

McDonald sister's cottage on the old airport road

As we passed the entrance to Furry Park Pitch and Putt, one of the Murphy brothers, either Andrew or Sean, let a few roars at us in fun, but we bolted, our nerves still on edge from the scattered drums incident a few minutes previously and we charged into Rolon Caravans to hide and catch our breath.

OSI June 1973

Monk's Bridge
Santry Woods
Lamberts House
Mc D'nlds Cottage
Bus Corner

Santry Woods, Rafts and Bulrushes.

We were now standing on the brow of the "Barrack Hill". Noel the brother spotted the speeding trolley opportunity at the same time as me. The Barrack Hill was a good 100 foot run of steep hill that ran past Lambert's gate at Claremont, and right up to the red and white-gate of Jack Roberts' old cottage.

View of Lambert's, now Little Venice restaurant, note Robert's gate

Chapter 7

I jumped first. "Baggsey first run down the hill," I shouted, already getting into the trolley, which was quickly relieved of it's four-drum cargo. The trolley wasn't great, the wheels were buckled from previous crashes and the rope controlled steering was a bit dodgy. Speeding down on a pathway only one foot from speeding oncoming motor traffic, was a bit un-nerving but we all got a few turns and we all survived. After the speeding trolley stuff had passed the expedition duly marched on with the four GTX oil drums now back on board. The trolley spin on the Barrack Hill was a small distraction but the prospect of floating on a raft was getting us all excited, oh yes, the holy grail awaited us.

Everyone except Johnny Darcy, came in through Roberts' gate crossing past the river which flowed under the road. Jack Roberts had long since moved up to Turnapin and there was nobody about to stop us. We cut in through the big red and white gate and walked around the long way behind the cottage. There was a beautiful smell of roses which seemed to be everywhere.

Santry Woods, Rafts and Bulrushes.

Once around the cottage we cut back up towards the bridge arch that led back under the main road. I was given the task of steering the trolley over the rough muddy terrain.

My brother Noel helped me pull the trolley along as we stumbled from rock to rock in the river trying to get it over. Unfortunately he got his feet wet for his efforts. The river crossing was a bit of a struggle with the trolley so we duly abandoned it mid stream and watched it spin away in the strong water flow. It was sad to see our faithful No 6 disappear under the bridge but I reckoned it would just jam the other side up towards Monk's bridge, so I could recover it another day.

Raft gang crossing the river. See Johnny Darcy beside Hilton sign

Chapter 7

As I mentioned already, Johnny Darcy had taken the scenic route doing a Tarzan call. "Ah..wah..ha..wah.ha.. wah.hawah..ha." He howled through two joined cupped hands, as per the actor Ron Ely, from the television series "Tarzan." We looked up to see Johnny swinging down from a height holding on to the support bars of the white "Hilton Hotel," double sided signs which were fixed into the ground at the wall beside the river bridge. Johnny was skinny but very wiry, and he was generally up for anything.

With each of us now carrying a drum, we all started running to the lake's edge. Noel's feet were wet already so he was quickly down to his bare feet. First things first, we needed to get the big pallet that was floating about 15 feet out from the water's edge. Fortunately for us it was lying close to a large half submerged tree trunk. If you have ever seen the everglades where people in small boats are weaving in and out under big rooted trees, all dark and misty, then you are getting what it was like. The place was full of bird song and the flapping of nervous wings as we disturbed the quiet upon our arrival. Noel, being barefoot already, was nominated to head out to try and get at the pallet. He was nervous and he had every right to be.

Santry Woods, Rafts and Bulrushes.

As soon as he got about five feet out along the tree trunk lying sideways in the water, there was a big splash as someone threw in a big stone close to him. As the water hit him he stood up, the trunk spun and in went Noel. He was shouting and I was immediately running into the water and Jesus it was stinking. As I trudged towards Noel, he got his balance and he stood up in about two feet of water. He was F'in and blinding at Johnny who had thrown the rock, but before long, with the danger passed, everyone was laughing, including him.

We assessed the situation, we were wet anyway so Noel and me continued on out, skipping from trunk to branch trying to grab that elusive pallet. With us two in the water, that left four at the water's edge. We could hear shouting in the distance and suddenly it was getting closer. We weren't the only ones in the Woods.

As the group came closer we saw that it was a bunch of younger kids from Santry village. I recognised two young Hanleys, Francis and Vincent with Gerry McCabe and a blonde haired Terry Clarke who were all running with a dog, who in the excitement came into the water towards me and Noel. The dog retreated quickly and the poor thing was covered in the foul smelling mud. With the dog out they scarpered quickly shouting a few choice words as they departed.

They were probably more afraid of us Turnapin lads than we were of them. If there had been a few more older ones with them, we were in trouble. They regarded Santry Woods as their territory, but thankfully this time they had retreated. Back in the water we managed to get hold of the pallet and we pushed it back towards the others. I wasn't impressed with the rock incident and I suddenly thought of Ma's reaction when we would get home, we were soaked and smelly, we were going to get it!

Chapter 7

With the pallet out of the water, we slipped the four oil drums underneath, one on each corner. Noel Murphy stepped in with the hammer and nails and did what he had to do. He hammered at least two into the pallet which pierced into each drum. They seemed sturdy enough, but as we lifted the pallet the drums just slid straight off the nails, hit the ground and rolled towards the waters edge! Some of us were laughing, then Derek Madden suggested we reposition the drums back onto the nails and tie them in place with rope and twine. Good thinking on Derek's behalf. Within minutes we were on the verge of launching the "Raft" that would make us sailors and seafarers and the excitement was building. At this stage poor Noel was really soaked, but at least my teeshirt was still dry.

Although it was summertime and quite warm, the cold water and thick shade kept us freezing. Cold wet clothes didn't help so Noel decided to take off his wet smelly tee shirt. We dragged the raft over to the edge and we pushed it in and yes it was floating. Johnny jumped on first, getting his balance really quickly and he was away. We were jumping and cheering, as Johnny moved himself along using a big stick he had found on the bank. Within a couple of minutes he had reached the Island and he was still dry. He got off, did his Tarzan cry again and then jumped back on and started back towards us.

I noticed that we had positioned the open nozzles of two drums under the water line, so in fact the raft was already sinking. Johnny was blissfully unaware, but within 20 seconds the raft was lopsided and capsizing. Johnny was making a meal of it, then "Splash" in he went as well. I was happy now. At least me and Noel weren't the only ones wet. We pulled out the raft, reset the drums, but Noel Murphy's nail holes were now the problem. We plugged them with twigs but the small nail holes were still not completely watertight.

Santry Woods, Rafts and Bulrushes.

As we relaunched again we knew we were in a race against time. All of us, with the exception of Gerry Madden, ended up in the water. This was important, since he had the matches because he smoked. We didn't care because we had finally built a raft that would float. With us all on the island, we decided to go native in the Jungle. We gathered up wood and dry grass and within minutes we had a fire going, it was now time to start drying our stinking wet clothes beside a stinking smokey fire!

When the smoke cleared and the firewood was roaring red, it was lovely and warm to our front but freezing at our backs. Red faced and toasting we positioned our clothes on standing sticks close to the fire and waited. Now, if we had stopped to think about it, there wasn't really any point in trying to dry the clothes at all, because we were on the island, with a sunken raft so there was no way back, except wading through the water again. With darkness falling, the glowing fire looked really cosy as it burned brightly, giving off a few bursts of sparks every now and then, especially if we disturbed it by throwing on more wood. Noel Murphy had broken a few Bulrushes and set them on fire. As they burned they cast shadows in all directions, including our faces which made them a little grotesque and creepy in the half light. Santry Woods was a spooky place for me and

Chapter 7

I had heard the story of the "sodden path" from my father. This story had been passed down from my grand uncle, Tom Kavanagh, who once lived on Bullock Hill in Santry Woods. Once on this path after nightfall, you would travel around in circles on this "sodden path" until daybreak the next morning. I figured we were in enough trouble already so I called an end to the day's adventure.

We poured water on the fire and it was really cold immediately, so cold in fact that I started shivering and doing that "Fa,Fa,Fa" with my teeth on my lips. Our feet were freezing as we squeezed them into our unforgiving cold wet rubber boots. We gathered up all our stuff, held what we could shoulder high to avoid the water as we waded out from the island. The sinking raft had hidden itself beside a half submerged tree trunk as if was sulking and ashamed that it had let us down for the crucial home crossing. On looking clumps of bulrushes seemed to mock the whole scene. We cut under the mainroad bridge and headed home through Geraghy's fields, starving and stinking of stagnant water and smoke. I spotted the red back board of our No 6 trolley in the distance jammed tight at Monk's low bridge. There would have to be another time for trolley salvage work.

By the time we hit Dunne's corner we were being met by excited on coming messengers. The word was out that we were in trouble for all sorts of things. Spilling a drum of oil, nearly causing car crashes, smoking in the Woods, running around with no clothes on, the list was growing but we just didn't care. We were sailors now and had floated on water and conquered the lost islands of Santry Woods.

Santry Woods, Rafts and Bulrushes.

As part of the creation of Santry Park in 2004 the lake was dredged and cleaned. The islands were reinstated.

Chapter 7

View of Barrick hill today looking back towards Turnapin. See Carley's pine trees in the distance

CHAPTER 8

Match of the Day, back in the Day

During the 1950's Turnapin Lane had developed a great reputation with the Starlights Gaelic football team. They had a huge local following and they were the very first organised football team to come out of the 36 Turnapin Cottages. They burst on the Dublin GAA scene when they won the Thomas Ashe Minor cup in 1952. Local involvement with this team, however, faded in the late 1960's and soccer became the game of choice for us Turnapin lads. During the summertime when the evenings got long and bright, we never stopped playing soccer and there was always a game going on somewhere.

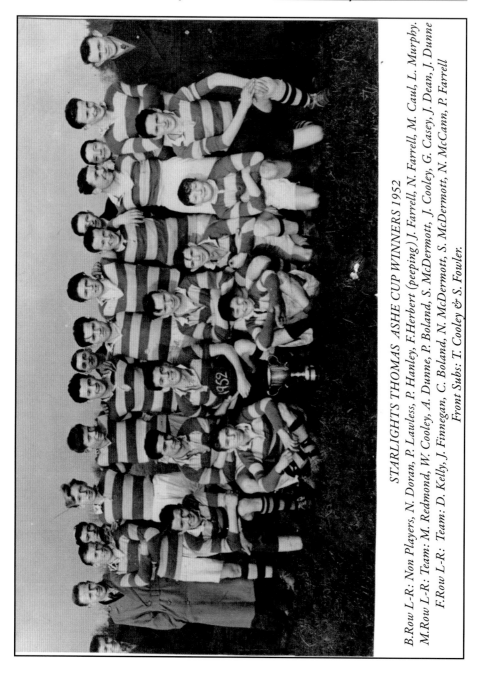

STARLIGHTS THOMAS ASHE CUP WINNERS 1952

B.Row L-R: Non Players, N. Doran, P. Lawless, P. Hanley, F.Herbert (peeping) J. Farrell, N. Farrell, M. Caul, L. Murphy.
M.Row L-R: Team: M. Redmond, W. Cooley, A. Dunne, P. Boland, S. McDermott, J. Cooley, G. Casey, J. Dean, J. Dunne
F.Row L-R: Team: D. Kelly, J. Finnegan, C. Boland, N. McDermott, S. McDermott, N. McCann, P. Farrell
Front Subs: T. Cooley & S. Fowler.

Chapter 8

The football games back then had 6 possible locations. Dunne's corner, Carley's field (back of the Orchard Wall), Dean's garden (rear of No 8), Madden's garden (rear of No 29), Barney Bolands (beside McGuirk's river), and lastly Geraghty's field. We tried to avoid the terrace itself because of the paths and the gardens which we had to avoid kicking the ball into. We had a few football baddies in the terrace and they were "Gocky Poocher" in No 31 (Mrs Redmond), Kitt Finn in No 17, and the Granny Cassidy in No 5. If you "Canted" the ball into their gardens it was goodbye ball and the game was over. A golden rule in Turnapin football was that if you kicked the ball into a garden, you had to jump in and get it yourself, very quickly!

No 17 Finn's

No 31 Redmond's

Match of the Day, back in the Day

When the Murphy's came out in force (they had enough for there own football team), the game would move down into the terrace and we would have one goal at Doran's big gate (No 7) and the other at Murphy's big gate (No 32). Then the Murphy sisters and their friends would decide that they wanted the space outside their place to skip, so our football game had to go back up to Dunne's corner. The Murphy sisters Breda, Marie, Cathleen, Geraldine and Lillian Murphy usually got what they wanted, with Mrs Murphy looking on and enjoying the bit of skit.

The Murphy family, No 32.
L-R, Bill Murphy, Lillian in arms, Agnes Murphy, Dessie in arms, Breda,
Cathleen and Peter. Front L-R, Marie, Noel, Geraldine and Liam.

Chapter 8

The scores in all these games was never 4 to 3, it was always 26 to 24 after 2 hours of noisy fast football. Then someone would shout out "next goal the winner," usually coming from the losing team and the game then went into hyper drive until the killer goal was scored. The goal posts were the usual spare jumpers and these caused all sorts of problems with disputed goals. A direct hit scattering the jumper usually counted as a wide. Other aspects of these games were there was no offside rule and we always played with a "fly" (outfield) goalkeeper especially if the numbers were low. With no offside rule this encouraged "hatching" around the goalmouth waiting for the overlap and goals got by these "hatchers" were really despised. "F'in hatcher" was the usual chant and a guaranteed heavy tackle on the goal scorer when the game resumed.

Dunne's corner was always very popular for the Sunday afternoon games. The "Doc" Roche was always a great man for joining into the middle of these games as he was passing by on his way back from Kealy's after the Sunday morning session.

He would come along, usually with jacket slung over his shoulder, walking with the head down as if he hadn't even noticed the game in progress. Then out of nowhere he would run at the ball pushing and tackling as he went. He would do a running commentary as the younger lads from both sides would be tackling him. Then, in an instant, the "Doc" would be gone, running on down the road to where he lived in No 26. He real name was Seamus Roche and he was a lot older than us. He was a gentleman who was always had a wave or a word for everyone. He worked in Gerry O'Brien's sweet factory up in Santry Village. He walked up and back to Santry everyday so he was a fit as a fiddle, despite being fond of the cigarettes. Like many of the younger generation in Turnapin he died way before his time.

Dunne's Corner ready for football

Chapter 8

The obvious draw back about Dunne's corner for football games was the road traffic. In general we knew most of the people who were passing through. We had Ned Fowler in his famous Morris Minor with the bale of hay on the back seat. There was Martin Galvin in his black Ford popular and speeding through us, we would have Claire Leavy looking straight ahead and never waving. Mr Burke, the school teacher, who lived past Jones was one to watch out for as well, his eye sight wasn't the best so we took no chances. Jimmy Dean's Austin A40 and his brother Brendan's Ford Std came through us as well. Their brother Arthur had a dark navy Cortina and it was probably the cleanest car I have ever seen. It glistened in the sunshine as it made it way, slowly, up and down the lane. My own family with their Mercedes taxi cars caused a few game hold ups because they always rolled down their windows to talk to us. Jerry Heeney and Tommy Carolan weaved through us on their motorbikes. All in all, traffic was light, so the games here were only held up every now and again.

Ned Fowler and his trusty grey Morris Minor. The Fowler farm milking shed is behind him

Match of the Day, back in the Day

Ford Cortina MK 2

Austin A40

Ford Zephyr 6

Mercedes 190

Ford Popular

Match of the Day, back in the Day

L - R : Alan Dean, Sharon Dean, Terry Dean with brother Raymond

One of the "cool" car drivers who often stopped our games when he was passing by was Ray Gunning from Clonshaugh. Once he drove through us, very slowly, in a blue Zephyr Ford, with a set of cow horns on the front bonnet and a blond in hot-pants sitting in the passenger seat. Another of his cars was a big white Zephyr Ford 6 and it even had an on board Television. Ray was a real gadgets man. He part owned a Discoteque in Dublin city called "The Apartment." He would drive past us on the way to his home in Clonshaugh near Jolly's Hill. I remember he wore turtle neck sweaters, dark glasses and of course the classic sixties pop star long hair.

At one time he was part of a "covers" band called "The Penguins." Another member of this band was Brendan Redmond from No 24 in Turnapin Lane. In the early days Brendan was a good friend of my uncle Joseph. Naming pop groups after animals was all the rage in the 1960's. Just think about it, The Beatles, The Monkees, The Byrds, The Animals, The Turtles so why not the "The Penguins"?

Chapter 8

This band played in local halls around Malahide and Coolock. Shanel College was one of their popular venues. They sometimes could be heard over in Gunning's house in Clonshaugh, practising all the hit songs of the time. They may not have realised it at the time but there was an American group from the 1950's already called "The Penguins" who had a massive hit with the song "Earth Angel."

Match of the Day, back in the Day

There were two other older "blokes" around on the Turnapin football scene and they organised a lot of the games. These were Johnny Joyce and Jim Finglas. These were city slickers to us and hence their interest was in the soccer rather than the Gaelic football. Johnny had married local girl Marie McCormack and Jim had married Jean Darcy. Jean was Johnny and Paul Darcy's older sister. Johnny Joyce worked close by in Rolon Caravan, while Jim Finglas was a "Singer" sewing machine technican. These two always seemed to be up for a match and they brought a little bit of order to our chaotic games. I suppose you could call them our very first managers. These were very vocal on the ball, shouting as you tackled them trying to put you off with their commentaries. Johnny Joyce in particular was always at this carry on.

Jim and Jean Finglas

Johnny and Marie Joyce

Chapter 8

When ever there was a match on these two were always in the thick of it. When traffic got heavy we had to move from Dunne's corner and Carley's was the next choice. This was a great venue because the orchard wall was a bounce back wall, so there was no side line which kept the game going better. It had one severe drawback however and that was losing the ball. If it went over the eight foot wall, it was gone. This was the ultimate dare.

The Carleys never really bothered with us playing in their fields, but going into the orchard after balls and running through their Strawberries and Rubarb was going too far. They had a dog who roamed this orchard and his name was Coalie Carley. Once you heard him barking there was no way anyone would go in.

Back with Johnny and Jim who would be there picking the teams, they would be coaching and giving instructions as well. They even did a bit of "dispute resolution". During these games there was always a bit of wild tackling from the less skillful and I remember once when a fight between my brother Noel and the late Andrew Roberts started, thank God Johnny Joyce was there to stop it.

There was always a few players that every one wanted on their team and Andrew Roberts was one of these. Fast, wiry, and most of all cocky, as he left you for dead with his fancy footwork. Johnny Darcy was another "Twinkle Toes". Once my cousin Hubert Brudell, Breda Boland's son, came and stayed for the whole summer. He shot straight into the top three on the first pick list. He was good. He never said much he just played the game. He had great speed and ball control and he could do the three "up downs" just tipping the ball from foot to knee, to head and back down again. Along with his english accent he was our very own curly topped "Roy of the Rovers."

Paul "Fodger" Murphy, his older brother Liam "Foreigner" Murphy, and Paulie Heeney (sprat) were another few bright sparks. I was mid-table, along with young Terry "Deaners" Dean, Gerry "Garter" Madden, Noel "Hacker" Murphy, Derek "Senate" Madden, Eddie "Vintan" Madden, John "Clonlure the big hure" Connolly and the brother Noel. We would get picked after the first three best players were already picked on each side.

Down among the sprats were Anto Murphy, Paul "Herrin'ner" Darcy, Willie "Booney" Heeney, David Cooley, Dessie Murphy, Stephen Pepper, Stephen Cooley and John Timmons. All of these were in the "you can have the rest" section. Willie Heeney in particular had a "tease" fuse about 3 seconds long and would go on for the whole game giving out about who he was playing with and what a "F*$Fing crap team they were." I can still picture him sulking off across Eddie Madden's Garden crying as he went, shouting back abuse as he

Chapter 8

was being teased, hence his nickname "Booney" because he cried so much! He also had a curious habit of chewing his teeshirt if he was upset.

Postscript: Nearly 40 years later after they settled in the new Turnapin Green which was built in 1975, I regulary meet Johnny Joyce and Jim Finglas and we talk about those famous "Match of the Day" football games that took place way back in the day, in Turnapin Lane.

In the late 1980's and 1990's there was a resurgence of the Starlights Gaelic Football in Turnapin Lane when a good crop of local players came along together and carried on the tradition of great Turnapin footballers. Other teams who played them would often ask, "Is there something in the water out there?" Oh Yes, they were tough!

Groovy baby, Jimmy Roberts and the "Doc" Roche on O'Connell St.

Match of the Day, back in the Day

STARLIGHTS FINGAL LEAGUE late 1980's

Back.Row L-R: P. Carrick, S. Cooley, D. Cooley, D. Murphy, N. Murphy, K. Price, A.McAllister, E. Crosby, A. Murphy, W. Curtis.
Front Row L-R: I. Cooley, P. Mohan, D. Murphy, G. McAllister, A. Cooley, J.Caul, S. Duffy, P. Darcy.

STARLIGHT'S FINGAL LEAGUE early 1990's

Back Row L-R: S. Duffy, A. Murphy, J. Caul, P. MaCallorum, A. McAllister, D. Duffy, R. Duffy, D. Singleton, G. McAllister
Front Row L-R: J. McDonagh, G.Virgoe, D. Caul, P. Mohan, B. Crane, A. Cooley, W. Curtis, D. Coleman.

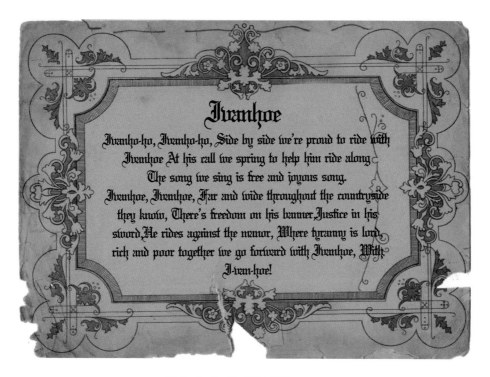

Ivanhoe

Ivanho-ho, Ivanho-ho, Side by side we're proud to ride with
Ivanhoe At his call we spring to help him ride along
The song we sing is free and joyous song.
Ivanhoe, Ivanhoe, Far and wide throughout the countryside
they know, There's freedom on his banner,Justice in his
sword,He rides against the manor, Where tyranny is lord,
rich and poor together we go forward with Ivanhoe, With
I-van-hoe!

CHAPTER 9

Swords, Slings & Bows 'n' Arrows.

When the adventures of the previous summer had long since faded to a distant memory, we found ourselves in early June, on the verge of another summer holiday. It was 1969 and we were all a year older. Early in the year, U.T.V. had started running a repeat of their 39 episode 'Ivanhoe' television series starring Roger Moore as the 12th century knight Sir Wilfred Ivanhoe. Another "Olde English" series, 'The Adventures of Robin Hood' starring Richard Green was already years on the go, so it was inevitable that we would eventually take up the cause of the down-trodden peasants against the evil English kings, including the hated Sheriff of Nottingham.

147

Swords, Slings & Bows 'n' Arrows.

Living on the east coast of Ireland we were living in Multi-Channel land, picking up all the "foreign" English stations and if you had the required "Hay-rake" on the roof, you could get them for free.

This hay-rake description of the TV aerial is attributed to Patsy "Spainy" McCann a famous local character who once fought Collins' bull after a few pints in May Murtaghs' Public house (Kealys) way back in the day. After he was gored by the bull, he ended up getting skin grafts from his rear end to his forearm. If he felt like he needed attention as he sat supping pints in the local pubs, he would hold up his forearm and plant a kiss on it. He would then make the statement, "I am the only man in this pub who can kiss his arse while I am still sitting on it." This always managed to get a few laughs. These T.V. aerials if turned the right way would get you access to UTV and BBC, oh yes, two stations for the price of none!

Chapter 9

Richard Green as Robin Hood

To answer this call to arms, Swords, Slings, Bows and Arrows were our weapons of choice. This rebellion of the great unwashed would start out as a united force against the English, but end up in a civil war breaking out between the bottom and the top of Turnapin Lane. Sound familar? Oh yes, in typical Irish style, cousin would fight cousin, friend would fight friend, all along established territorial boundaries which were in fact our back gardens.

At eleven years of age I was already a seasoned Bow 'n' Arrow maker. Da had taught us how to make them all and we got what we needed in the small trees at the end of our garden. Slings or "Gatts" as they were sometimes called, were never really that popular and were only used by us to get "our eye in" shooting at empty tin cans or unfortunate crows perched, squawking on nearby electricity poles in Johnny Farrell's garden. They were considered far too dangerous for local

warfare. To make a sling you needed a fork cut from a tree, rubber strips cut from an inner car tube, some chicken wire and the tongue from an old leather shoe. When put together and shot off with small stones in the pouch they were lethal. During our skirmishes we often used slings to shoot off rolled up muck balls high into air, to rain down on our enemies lying in the long grass. When we were making the bows, a long piece of hazelwood about six foot long was required and we pared a six inch piece in the center down to the bare wood so we could get a really tight grip on the bow with our gripping hand. The arrows were at three least three foot long and as straight and thin as you could get them.

My mother hated all of this "Slings, Bows 'n' Arrows" carry-on because her older brother Sean had lost an eye from an arrow, shot by a homemade bow when he was just a young boy back in the 1940's.

Our summer holidays from school had only just started when we started meeting at the end of Murphy's garden arranging sword fights and archery competitions with the homemade bows and arrows. A football was placed on top of a square wooden stake and from about 30 feet we would have three arrow shots at the ball. I was a pretty good shot and there was a lot of showing off by everybody especially if there were one or two young maid Marions around the place. The first archery sequence was easier, just shooting while standing still. The second one involved shooting as you walked. As you stepped along you then knelt down and shot the arrow, holding the bow cross-ways, all in the same movement, just like it was in the television battle scenes. This was very difficult to do as the ground underfoot was very uneven and thick with long grass.

Swords, Slings & Bows 'n' Arrows.

Old dart boards were recycled and hung from low hanging tree branches. The arrows when fired would hit them full on which made a very satisfying thud as they bounced back from the board. This would make them spin and so, even more difficult to hit.

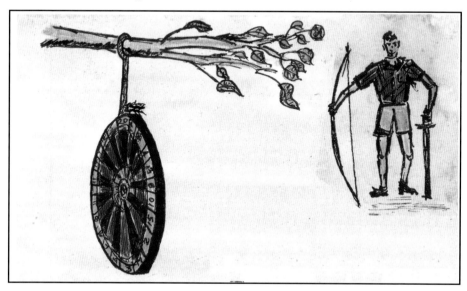

This was really great fun and we got hours of enjoyment with it. We also had "real" sword fights, complete with shields which were the lids of the 5 gallon oil drums from our yard. There was a lot of "charging" around as if on horseback and if you had the knack, you could be seen pulling back the head of your imaginary horse as if it was about to bolt off somewhere to do something very brave, like have your dinner for instance!

At some point you had to leave and go home, but you always stayed in character. First you slid your sword through your belt, usually an old tie, then your head through the bow over your shoulder, then with arrows in hand you made off as if you were on the back of your

Chapter 9

trusty steed. During the "jumping along" movement through the long grass your sword could swing forward or get jammed between your legs causing you considerable pain in the groin area not to mention the embarrassment of falling over. One minute you would be a graceful knight singing the Ivanhoe song as you jumped along heading for home, only to disappear in a comical heap with all your armoury crashing about you in a shambles.

I remember well the exact circumstances of the civil war breaking out and it was during a general sword fight or "Jousting" competition that got out of hand at the end of Murphy's garden. The two fencers were Jimmy "Skitcher" Heeney and one of the younger Murphy brothers, either Paul "Fodger" or Dessie. I am going to opt for Paul Murphy, as Dessie was a little too young at the time. The protocol during the sword fights was once you got touched by the tip of your opponent's wooden sword on the upper torso you were dead.

No long drawn out death scenes, you had to fall down dead, as if hit by lightning, out of the game, gone. Hits to the arms and legs didn't count. These wooden swords were about 3ft long and roughly 2" by 1" thick in light pallet wood. They were sanded down with sand paper to remove any dangerous splinters and no pointy edges were allowed. They had hand protection by way of a small piece of wood nailed crossways to stop your opponent's sword sliding down and hitting your hand. If you used only one nail the guard wasn't as strong because it could swivel on the single nail when struck. Even worse the swiveling wooden guard would pinch the fleshy skin between your thumb and first finger, Ouch! it really did hurt.

Jimmy Heeney was a bit taller than Paul and during this particular sword fight, his guard did swivel and his hand was pinched when little Paul struck down on Jimmy's sword hand. While he was nursing his pinched hand, Paul moved in for the kill and made heavy contact on his torso. Instead of dropping the sword and falling down dead, Jimmy went off on a "sevener" swiping at all and sundry with his sword, cursing and crying at the same time. To be fair to Paul, he pulled back, dropped his sword and ran away from Jimmy who had just gone berserk. A young Terry Dean was standing by holding his sword as he was due to fence the winner but he just dropped his sword and ran away.

Two younger brothers of the two combatants, who were there as well, Dessie Murphy and young Willie Heeney took up their brothers cases and before long everyone was getting involved. It all got a bit "hold me back", or "I'll get out me temper" as everybody threw down their weapons and started grabbing each other by the scruff of the neck and pulling each other onto the ground in a head lock. There was even a few sly "boots" thrown in for good measure. In all there was about a dozen of us involved in this brief skirmish.

It all only lasted a few minutes because old Jem Darcy, Johnny's Da, let a few shouts at us from his small vegetable garden which was close by. He was standing there digging a few drills in his trademark white vest. Mr Darcy was a legend to us younger lads. Often times we would come across him sawing a bit of wood in his corrugated shed. In belted trousers and his white vest he would gather us in close with his low voice and start off one of his many war stories. He usually began with "Lads, have I ever told you the story of the battle of the boiling water? Oh yeah, I can see it all now, there I was, up to me neck in wild blood thirsty BAA-LOO-BAAS. At least twenty or maybe thirty of them, all with spears and shields, mad fiery eyes, bones through their noses and not a stitch of clothes on them. I was holding them back until our lads got back into the trenches, "Then" he said, with his piecing blue eyes wide open looking at us all one by one, "me old pal, Bill Cooley jumped up and charged in with his bayonet to the ready and saved the day. Oh yeah, only for the bold Bill Cooley, I was done for," "A great Tipperary man" Jem went on, starting the marching song "It's a long way to Tipperary, it's a long way to go" in his best deep voice. He would hold out his hands and say "look men, I can still feel the fear in me hands to this day," as he held them out for us to inspect, exaggerating the shaking in them. Mrs Darcy would be at the sink, looking out from the kitchenette window laughing out loud at the carry on that Jem was going on with us. "Jesus Jem, will you leave them lads alone and bring in some sticks when you're finished acting the feckin' maggot out there."

Mr and Ms Darcy

Swords, Slings & Bows 'n' Arrows.

"Better go lads, the big chief of the BAA-LOO-BAAS has spoken," winking and giving a mock army salute in Mrs. Darcy's direction.

Like her husband Jem, Mrs. Darcy always seemed to be in good form, she had a dimpled face that lit up when she was smiling. Her name was Lena but I always addressed her as Mrs. Darcy.

Jem had us all believing that he and Bill Cooley had fought in the Congo in the 1950's out in Africa. Both of them did serve in the Irish Free State army but were long gone before the Congo trouble started. It was highly likely that neither of them ever fired a single shot in anger. Jem was stationed in Santry Demesne

Jem Darcy, 7th Infantry Battalion, 3rd Row, 3rd from left

during the 2nd World War, while Bill Cooley had served years earlier in the 1930's up in Clancy Barracks on infirmary road in the early 1930's. It was here that Bill had met my grandmother, Cathleen Kavanagh from no 21 Turnapin Cottages, who was working there as a house maid to an officer. By all accounts she was a lovely woman with herself and Bill making a handsome couple. Sadly, she died in 1954, four years before I was born.

Jem Darcy used to start a rhyme really earnestly, "Young Cooley, you're a grand Toppin' chap with brains to burn, aren't you?, well answer me this if you can,"

Grandparents Bill and Cathy Cooley

If it took a man a week to walk a fortnight, how many eggs in a barrel of grapes?" I knew the answer because he always asked the same question. It was none. Jem was a decent hardworking man, one of the old school and by all accounts he was a great scaffolder.

Swords, Slings & Bows 'n' Arrows.

Mr. Darcy's intervention was enough to break up our little skirmish and it fizzled out pretty quickly. Surprisingly, however, the walking away and breaking up wasn't friendly at all. There was no hand shaking, no laughing it off, as the blood was still boiling and curiously we were all still up for it. I got a bit of a bloody nose because Andrew Roberts had grabbed me in a head lock, but when my brother Noel jumped up on his back, he released me sharpish. Noel was a tough nut even then and if he got that look in his eye you were in big trouble.

Oh yes, feathers had been severely ruffled and harsh name calling was engaged in on both sides. "Bleedin' knacker, Spud Murphy" somebody said, "Smelly arse" shouted another "Yeah, youzes Cooleys think you're great," "Yeah, bleedin Eejits." All in all it was pretty harmless stuff. Then out of the blue the gauntlet was thrown down when someone piped up saying, "Let's sort all this out tomorrow, right here in the back gardens." Yeah, bring all you have,' someone shouted, "We'll be ready!"

"Yeah, we'll be bleedin here, 3 o'clock, don't worry about that" was the quick reply. It was really amazing, only 10 minutes earlier we were all having a bit of a lark then it had all changed, " Changed utterly and a terrible beauty was born" to use a quote by the great W.B.Yeats.

The older people around Turnapin at the time would say "none of that tomfoolery" or "that horse-play always ends in tears" and this time it had, big time. This was the first and only time, that all the lads in Turnapin had ever really fallen out on such a grand scale and now we were on the verge of a civil war. I was frightened about it but curiously looking forward to the forthcoming battle.

Chapter 9

As we walked away, heading back to our big shed across the back gardens I noticed how long the grass was and how easy it would be to take cover in. We passed over Roche's small wire fence and I realised that this would be the dividing line on the battlefield for "The battle of Turnapin Lane" the following day. We started running because the others had started running after us, shouting at us, name calling again, and shooting a few arrows at us. "BAK- BAK-BAK-BAK-BAK" Johnny Darcy called out imitating a chicken as we retreated. Noel picked up one of the arrows and was just about to break it when I shouted "Don't, Noel, keep it for tomorrow, we are going to need lots of them tomorrow." Noel broke it anyway and started running back towards them throwing it in their direction, only to be met with a cacophony of derisory cheers as it fell well short of where they were.

I looked back and it seemed like there was loads of them, while we were only four! Noel, myself, Jimmy and Willie Heeney. Jesus we needed re enforcements badly and we needed them quickly.

When we reached our yard, we went into the big shed and sat down on a few old car seats that were lying around. By this time it had dawned on me that two of my best friends, Noel Murphy and Johnny Darcy were now my enemies and this upset me no end. "No time for this" I thought to myself. "War has been declared and first things first." I said out-loud, "we are going to need loads of arrows and a few bows to fire them with, lets get going."

Noel had done his sums as well as me and piped up "There's only four of us and ten of them, they are going to bleedin' marmelize us tomorrow." What about Gerry, Derek and Daithi Madden?" he asked, "Do you reckon they will come with us?"

Swords, Slings & Bows 'n' Arrows.

I replied confidently, "No problem, no doubt about it." Jimmy Heeney added, "I have a big Gatt and I can make a bag of muck balls, they will use the old Morris Minor car lying up in Mahony's Garden as a forward base, so I will drop my shots in on top of them while they are there." "Great idea, Skitch" I said "Good thinking Batman!"

Frontline troops

L to R

John Cooley

Paul Curtis

Gerard Cooley

Skitcher had a lovely set of white teeth when he smiled. "Yes brilliant" I went on, "now let's get down to Maddens and we can get the wood for the Bows 'n' Arrows along the way down, the ditches are full of them". With that, my young first cousin, John Cooley wandered in, he was living with us in No. 21 at the time. His father, John Cooley, was my father's older brother. Young John had two younger brothers Gregory and Ivor, but they were too young for battle but I counted him in and we all headed down to Maddens. All except Willie Heeney, that is, he headed home for some fried chips that his mother Chris was cooking. We could smell them from down the garden and they were the nicest chips you ever tasted. I asked Willie to follow us on with some chips, he replied "Yeah Right!, do I look bleedin' stupid?"

Chapter 9

Being June, the weather was glorious as we ran down to Maddens around on the back road. The initial anger had dissipated a little and we started looking out for branches we could use for the bows and arrows as we went along past Curran's ditch. We had nothing with us to cut them, but I knew we could get all the saws and hatchets we needed in Maddens. Ned Madden was a great man for timber tools.

Curran's ditch with Madden's cottage in the distance

We knocked on the door and Mrs. Madden, known to us as Dolly McGuirk answered it. McGuirk was her maiden name and she had been born in this house. "The lads are down the garden or in the shed I think" she replied softly as she closed the door. I knew her well because it was me that came down most of the time to buy her eggs for Ma when she needed them. I heard a bit of a commotion in the shed so we headed there and found Derek Madden working at a bicycle wheel fixing a puncture.

161

Swords, Slings & Bows 'n' Arrows.

He was holding a half inflated bicycle tube under the water in a basin trying to see small bubbles rising up, indicating where the hole in the tube was. He wasn't getting very far because he had no bicycle pump. He was trying very hard to blow the tube up through the valve with his mouth. This was very tricky because, firstly you had to grip the valve with your teeth, then you had to hold the inner plunger in the valve down with your tongue as you blew the air into the tube. With weak puffing you couldn't really get a whole lot of air pressure up, so this led to weak and faint air bubbles from the hole in the tube.

Derek was bent very low trying to see any bubbles coming up and he was not looking very happy. He jumped straight up as we got to the open shed door. "This feckin' tube is driving me Jayzus feckin' mad," as he flung it out of the shed, nearly hitting me in the face as it hopped off the inside of the shed door. He stepped back in surprise when he saw our little group appearing in the doorway of the shed.

Incidentally, we had just grown by another two members because two cousins of mine, Hubert and Glenn Brudell had caught up with us on the back road just past Curran's house. These were Breda Boland's sons and she was my mother's sister.

They had just arrived from England on their "Summer Holidays" and we were all delighted to see them. "Oh yes" I thought "another pair of hands was really welcome". Noel commented awkwardly, that as they were staying up in Bolands, in no 33, with my aunt Chris at the top of the Lane beside Murphy's, they really should be fighting with the others. "No way, no way, they are with us," I protested, a little bit peeved by Noel's treachery. Hubert readily agreed, after all we were his cousins for Christ's sake. Hubert loved being in Turnapin Lane on his holidays. It was wild and free with plenty of "stuff" going on. His younger brother Glenn was like Gregory and Ivor Cooley the other cousins back in Turnapin, just a little too young for medieval warfare.

As Derek walked out of the shed he angerly kicked the basin of water that he had been using for the puncture mending out of his way, sending the water in all directions. "What's up?" he asked "What are ye all looking for?" Derek's face always got red when he was excited. "Derek" I said "we need you badly, we are in a war up in Turnapin and there's loads of them." I was very dramatic about it. "With who, for Jayzus sake?" Derek replied quickly, laughing and looking at Hubert and Glenn.

L to R: Jimmy Heeney, Gerard Cooley, Paul Curtis, David Cooley, Noel Cooley, Hubert Brudell

Swords, Slings & Bows 'n' Arrows.

"Who's are these fellas"? he enquired quickly, "That's Hubert and he is Glenn his brother," I said, "the cousins from England, they are home for a while in Turnapin." "Hug Bear, now that's a funny name" he said "No, No. H-u-b-e-r-t " I replied slowly, spelling it out as I went. Derek pulled in his horns and got a little embarrassed for both himself and Hubert who was just standing there smiling at him. It wasn't the first time Hubert had got a bit of teasing over his name. Derek went on "So who is this Turnapin war with anyway, its not with grumpy ould Kit Finn is it?" he laughingly exclaimed.

With that, Derek's older brother Gerry "Garter" Madden wandered out of the house with a cigarette in his hand as usual. He was just fourteen and was allowed to smoke in front of his Ma and Da. "Wow" I thought, if he was old enough to smoke, I hoped he was going to be on our side. Gerry piped up shyly, through the cigarette in the side of his mouth.

"He is only a cranky ould shite that fella Kit Finn, do you re-member he burst our ball last year because it went into his gar-den?" Gerry was right, it had happened but I replied "No, no, it's not with him, it's with the top of the lane lads up in Turnapin, we are going to sort it out tomorrow in the back gardens at 3 o'clock. We need as many arrows and stuff as you have and of course we need you to help us beat the shite out of them." Gerry replied, "Well I'm out for tomorrow morning, because I am working in P.J. Jones' doing a bit of cabbage planting with Johnny Farrell.

"It's tomorrow afternoon, you feckin' gobshite," Derek said "and you are in, we need you, so you better be there." Gerry nodded "ok fair enough, I'll be there, what do you want me to do?" as he flicked his

164

cigarette butt away. I could see Hubert was amazed that Gerry was actually smoking in front of his mother who was looking out the kitchen window. "We'll think of something" I said as I turned and asked Derek had he any arrows lying around. "funny you should ask," he replied, "but I was trying out something yesterday with a copper arrow head that I made using a piece of copper pipe, come around here and I will show you." We moved around to the side of the shed and there was a full solid wooden fence between themselves and McGuirks next door.

Derek rooted out his bow and picked up his "special arrow" and pulled it back slowly in the bow saying "Just watch, eight lat in from the left, first time." With that he let it go. "Whamz," it hit the lat, full on, but amazingly it stayed stuck into the wood. "Jesus" I shouted and we all ran to the arrow sticking in the lat. The arrow had two panel nails each side at the head, held in place with a piece of copper tube flattened out to grip the small nails in place.

He pulled it out and we all examined how he had done it. Hubert was really impressed with the arrow that "stuck" into things, but this wouldn't last long. Later on as we tried a few more out, Hubert wandered into the line of fire, only to get an arrow into the arm. I can still see the horrified look on his face as he ran towards us with the arrow stuck in his shoulder! We all consoled him, but it wasn't very deep and there was only two small holes for wounds. Dolly appeared out from the kitchen after hearing all the commotion and wiped poor Hubert's cuts with the foul smelling blue iodine. He looked like something from our American Civil War cards. I was going to get in trouble over this one.

CRUSHED BY THE WHEELS
MECHANICSVILLE, VA.—JUNE 26, 1862

American Civil War card

This new arrow was indeed a very dangerous weapon and there was no way we could use these for the battle of Turnapin the following day. Gerry Madden piped up saying, "I have an idea, lads, I will be your secret weapon tomorrow. I am going to be late anyway so I will fire some arrows across from the back road and when they give me a chase you can shoot at them as they run after me." Jimmy Heeney said he would join Gerry and he would have his sling, dropping muck balls in on them as well. A plan of attack was starting to develop and I liked it. Whether Gerry knew what his full plan was at this stage or not, I don't know but if he had told me what he was thinking of doing, I would have been terrified and said no way, of this I am completely sure. Gerry left us and armed with hatchets and hand saws we spent that whole

Chapter 9

evening making bows and arrows. We got the arrows from around the "Man from Uncle Den" in Barney Boland's field. We always stripped the bark off the arrow but left about six inches of it in place around the top. This helped the arrow come down head first because it was heavier. Noel the brother slyly pared a few points on some arrows but I blunted them, no points on arrows were allowed, rules of war had to be observed.

As we left for home with our bows and arm fulls of arrows, Derek asked me if it was alright to get the two Gunning brothers from Clonshaugh involved. Their names were Gerard and Christy and they attended the national school in Clonshaugh with the Madden brothers. My answer was "the more the merrier" and by all accounts these lads were a bit wild, which was exactly what we needed. Derek said he would slip down on his bike to them first thing the next morning. I did a quick count in my head and I reckoned we had at least ten, six better than the four we had started with only a few hours previously. Oh yes we were going to have a right go now!

It was nearly dark by the time we all got home to our house which was only a five minute walk back from Maddens. At this stage there was a search party out for young John Cooley, as well as our new arrivals from England. Before we parted we all had agreed to keep the battle the next day a secret. The meeting place was our big shed the following day at 12 noon, three hours before the battle would take place. Gerry Madden wouldn't be there in the shed for the start, he was to appear later at 3 o'clock on the back road for what would turn out to be the deciding action in the infamous "Battle of Turnapin Lane."

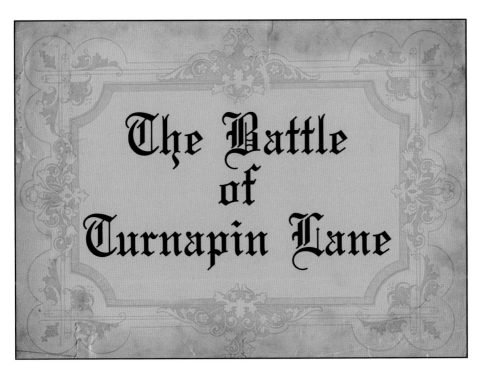

CHAPTER 10

The Battle of Turnapin Lane

I got up early next morning after a restless night of tossing and turning while dreaming about battles and swashbuckling sword fights. Noel slept like a log and was fast asleep as I slipped out of the bunk bed and down to the cold bedroom floor. It was a Saturday morning and the house was very quiet as I got myself dressed. Da had already left for work in the taxi to the airport and because it was summertime, the airport taxi rank would be "flyin" from early morning. Down in our kitchenette I quietly sat eating my three weetabix, drenched with lovely cold milk and the cream that gathered at the top of the bottle. While I was sitting there I spotted a pair of binoculars that Da had

The Battle of Turnapin Lane

up on top of the kitchen press. My uncle Willie, his eldest brother, said that some "Yank" had left them in his car and he had given them to Da to use while he was out hunting with his buddy Michael Caul.

I finished my grub, grabbed them quickly and headed down to the shed because I had a bright idea to get up onto the roof for a good overall view of the battlefield. The shed was very high and I had to get up using the frame of the window in the front of the shed which faced down our garden. There were never any ladders in our yard.

I brought my old blue "Q Bike" crash helmet with me, which at this stage was plastered with tiger heads from the Esso "Put a tiger in your tank" stickers. When Da got these for me down in the Esso station facing Barthleys, I would cut out the heads of the tigers and stick them everywhere, even my school books had them. By this time there was a big crack in the crash helmet but I would wear it during the battle anyway, it might deflect an incoming arrow or a potentially deadly sword strike! My imagination was really starting to run wild about the impending battle.

Up on the shed I got a great view of the battlefield and Jesus, it was big! Our back gardens were very long, maybe 200 yards or so. Our cottages were built in the 1930s and these gardens were big enough to allow people to grow vegetables and even keep hens and pigs in. All of this usually took place in the tops of the gardens and these were the nearest to the house. This meant the bottom half of all the gardens were not used by anyone, with the exception of McDermotts in no 35 on our side. They grew vegetables and even had big haycock in their garden. Once we burrowed into the middle of this haycock to play a game of Ludo and we proceeded to light a candle so we could see. Needless to say, we eventually managed to burn the haycock and that was another day on the receiving end of a good belting.

At one stage I remember a few cows grazing in McDermott's garden and they even made their own butter with the milk. McDermott's field belonged to this family. Johnny Darcy had an older brother called Jim who used to milk the cows in McDermotts and once he got a kick of a cow that he was attempting to milk there. Like his father, Jim was a great local character and a typical Turnapin lane man. Great fun and great sport, always a pactical joke or a wind up on the go from his little shop at the side of his father's house in no 30 Turnapin Lane, throughout the 1980's and 90's.

McDermott's garden was very close to the top of Turnapin, so their used piece didn't break the open space of the other gardens that were just let grow wild with long grass. Even at this point in time there was some confusion about who still owned the ends of their back gardens because the Council had a long term plan of buying the gardens from the owners one by one and building more council houses there. These houses, called Turnapin Grove, were finally built on these back gardens in the mid 1980s.

Back on the roof on the big shed, I sat there surveying the battlefield at great length. Furthest away I could see my grandad Boland's big pig-shed. Then one garden closer was Murphy's "Peacock" shed and this was a small low-level concrete pig shed with a corrugated roof. By this time Liam Murphy had converted it to very fancy Pigeon loft. I never remembered any pigs in either of them. Closer again was the black Morris Minor car wreck that was lying in Mahony's garden but this was still pretty far away. I swung around to have a close look at the end of our garden where there were lots of car and truck wrecks to be seen. One or two of them were in good shape easily good enough

The Battle of Turnapin Lane

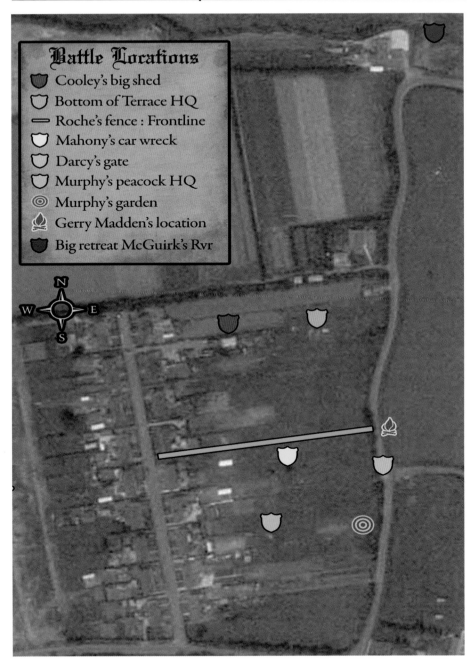

Battle Locations

- Cooley's big shed
- Bottom of Terrace HQ
- Roche's fence : Frontline
- Mahony's car wreck
- Darcy's gate
- Murphy's peacock HQ
- Murphy's garden
- Gerry Madden's location
- Big retreat McGuirk's Rvr

Chapter 10

for our battle HQ. There was a white 180 Mercedes that belonged to my Uncle Tom along with a wine coloured Ford Zephyr that we could use as well. These had doors that still opened and locked, so if things got really bad we could at least retreat and be safe in a locked car. I was thinking of everything.

The gardens that would be the battlefield itself, starting from ours, were McCanns next door, then Timmons, Hynes, Connollys, Roches, Peppers, Mahonys, Maddens, Darcys, Redmonds, Murphys, Bolands and Hanleys. All combined these were easily the size of two football pitches end to end. Unfortunately for us some of the gardens still had a low-lying boundary wire fence running up along and most of it was obscured by the long grass and so, very easy to trip over. To my left I scanned the bottoms of the gardens which bordered the back road from where Gerry Madden and Jimmy Heeney would later create confusion by launching a side attack on our unsuspecting enemies from the top of Turnapin.

I reckoned that they could get close enough to get in range at Darcy's gate so I needed to tell Jimmy Heeney that he and Gerry could get up that close without being seen because of the big hedge beside Darcy's Gate.

I took a break from battle planning for a minute and started to take in what was going on around me in Turnapin that particular summer's morning. I heard a very noisy Aer Lingus 737 Jet coming into land, Jesus is was loud. This was a new one that I hadn't noticed before. It glimmered and shimmering in the early morning sunlight as it glided into land like a big white swan with its wings tilting in the wind turbulence.

173

The Battle of Turnapin Lane

I had grown up with airplanes taking off and landing but visitors to Turnapin would stand open mouthed and amazed at the sights and the noise, but we didn't even notice it.

"Da would be waiting for people coming off that one," I thought to myself as I swung around to have a good look at Farrell's garden below me. Their garden was in full use and it looked perfect just like their front garden. They had cabbages and potatoes planted in neat drills the full length of the garden. The potatoes were just coming into flower and there were lots of white "cabbage" butterflies flitting about. With the binoculars I got a great close up of their scarecrow and Jesus it looked like Johnny Farrell himself. The scarecrow had Johnny's overalls and shirt on, but it looked like it was wearing old Mr. Farrell's trilby hat. I smiled to myself at the view, as bird song replaced the roar of the 737's engines, now safely landed. Over the hedge at the bottom of Farrell's garden to the left of the sewage pump-house I could see the chimney pot of Curran's house puffing out a faint stream of smoke. This hedge which ran the length of the Farrell's garden was bursting with Mayflower scent and the sound of birds chirping as they flew out of the hedge to rest on the phone wires which ran along the poles.

Milk Bottles at Curran's gate

Mr and Mrs Curran were an odd couple and had a black dog which was chained up most of the time. To us it had no name and it was just known as "Curransziz" dog. There was never any children about. She was a small woman who wore a red tea-cosy hat and she made jam with fruit she grew herself. I have a vague memory of speaking to her one day about "goosegob" (gooseberry) jam. I would have been in there delivering the milk with Charlie Hoystead. I usually left the milk bottles at the gate because of the dog but for some reason on at least one occasion I found myself inside the gate talking to her.

The Battle of Turnapin Lane

Mr. Curran was a tallish man with a cap and the word was he had fallen out with his brother who lived at the other end of the field along the old Swords road. His brother used to drive past us on the main road at the bus stop with his tractor trailer loaded with cabbage. He drove at a snail's pace and caused hold ups as he drove along, but he didn't care. He never ever said hello to us or anybody else for that matter, another local odd-ball, to be sure.

My gentle focus on Farrell's garden and Curran's cottage was broken when I heard some noise coming from the direction of Murphy's peacock, which was enemy H.Q. There was some movement there already and I excitedly adjusted my binoculars to have a closer look. As I fiddled with the adjustment screw I heard Noel grunting and grinding as he climbed his way up to the roof of the shed to join me. I leaned down and pulled him up. "Give us a go of them" he asked gruffly. "Hold on a minute will you ?" I answered, annoyed that he had found me so quickly, "I think there's something happening up at Murphy's peacock." It was about eleven o'clock at this stage and the tar based felt on the shed roof was starting to heat up under the glare of the morning sun. The smell of tar-pitch filled the air. Noel took the binoculars and starting scouring the distance for the source of the noise. "Look there" he pointed quickly "it's that cranky ould Gocky-Poocher, she is out having a pick and a gawk and she is throwing anything she finds into Murphy's garden next door. We'll give her something to look at today when we kick all their skinny arses." Noel had taken the binoculars down from his eyes and only when he was deadly serious did the slight turn or stare in his eye become noticeable. He was up for it alright.

Then we spotted a small group of lads coming in over Darcy's

Chapter 10

garden gate heading up to Enemy HQ at the peacock. They had just come down McDermott's car road. "Who are they?" I asked "Hold on" Noel replied, "let me see, yes I see them now, hold it, Johnny Darcy is there and there's a big lad with them and another smaller one, I don't know them." "Give here" I gestured to Noel for the binoculars, I got focused and couldn't believe my eyes. "Fecksake" I shouted "It's big Soss Wall", otherwise known as the "Grizzley" from Clonshaugh and that is Martin Crilly with them as well. They go to school with Johnny Darcy in Clonshaugh" I added. "I hope Derek has gone down to the Gunnings, we are really going to need them now." Just then a group went to meet them walking down from the Peacock in Murphy's Garden. I could see at least four Murphy brothers, Liam, Noel,

Brothers in arms, myself and Noel, 1969

Dessie and Paul. Andrew Roberts and Eddie Madden were there as well. Even Thomas Whelan a cousin of the Murphys from Swords had arrived. "Jesus H" I said, "they are really digging them up," I looked at Noel, "feck-sake" he said, "They are going to bleedin' kill us!."

The Battle of Turnapin Lane

Our terror was broken by Ma shouting out from the back door. "GGGGEEEERRRRAAAARRRRAAADDDDD" she called out at the top of her voice. "Jesus Ma" I said to myself in a low voice "Jesus, shut up or they will see us." Me and Noel flattened out quickly on the roof of the shed and rolled back from the edge to avoid been seen. Then again, "GEEERRRRAAAAARRRRAADDD." "Feckssake what does she want?" I said to Noel "Say nothing and stay quiet, she will stop eventually" Noel replied. I peeped out over the edge of the shed to see her coming down the yard with both Hubert and Glenn Brudell in tow. I noticed a third person with them and this was John Boland another young cousin home from England. He was Sean Boland's son and he was a little bit older than us. He was a wide London boy and a real live wire. He started imitating my mothers call in his distinct cockney accent. "Gerrriiiiddddd" he screamed, as he waved a big stick about that started the dog barking as well.

Noel whispered "If Ma catches us up here we are dead meat". "I know" I replied, "and if they don't stop shouting at us, they will hear it up at the Peacock and maybe come down for a closer look." We rolled back from the edge of the shed and just lay there like two dead corpses looking up at the brilliant blue morning sky. I heard our phone ringing up in the hall and with that we were saved.

Ma turned on her heels and headed back up to answer the phone. It's incredible now to think that only two people in the 36 Turnapin Cottages had phones, ourselves and Barretts (Cassidys) in No 5. Stephen Barrett drove a taxi and we had the coal business so we needed one for that. It was normal for some neighbours to knock at our door and ask to use our phone, most left some coins behind which we duly swiped. As well as that, people would ring our phone looking for such and such a person in Turnapin Lane and we would be sent to get them and again this was accepted as normal. Our phone no was 371399 and many a phone call came in from England in particular, with urgent messages for relatives here. See our William Cooley & Sons coal docket below from the 1970's. Note the spelling of Clochran, it was always a bone of contention in the area. Two other versions of the name are: Cloghran and Cloughran.

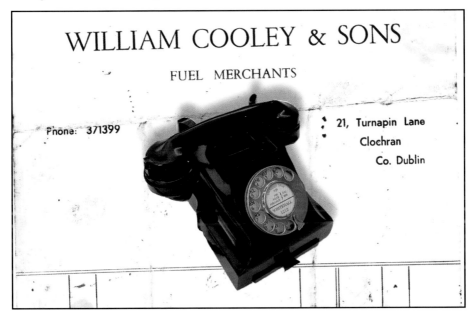

We waited until Ma went up to the house and then we peeped out over the edge to talk to John, Hubert and Glenn who were still standing around down below, playing with and hugging "Boy" our black and white dog. "Down in a minute" I said quietly, with none of them really sure where the sound was coming from. "Where the facking-ell are you mate?" John Boland shouted out and with that my mother shouted down, with her hand over the phone receiver. "John Boland, watch your tongue, or I'll tell your Jayzus' father." "Sorry Auntie May" he said sheepishly, "Sorry, but Gerridd and Noel made me say it, Auntie May," looking up at us and smiling. John was going to be a great help to us. He had been back the previous year and he stayed in No 33. The top of the terrace lads knew him and he was a tough cookie. Noel dropped down the binoculars to John who held his hands up to catch them. Back on the ground we gathered up our three cousins and headed down our garden to our HQ. Within a few minutes Willie and little "Paulie" Heeney had joined us. Potential cannon fodder I thought to myself.

BR L-R: Noel Cooley, Olive Heeney, Linda Cooley, Mary Heeney
FR L-R: David Cooley, Karen Cooley, Paul Heeney

The big shed

The Battle of Turnapin Lane

Wine Ford Zephyr similar to our HQ

We pulled open the stiff doors of the white car and scrambled in. The front windscreen was gone so the car seats were a bit damp and there was an overpowering smell of musty leather because the midday sun was now starting to bake the inside of the car as it beamed through the back windscreen. I wasn't happy that the front windscreen in our HQ was missing, so I had a close look at the wine Zephyr beside us, it had all the glass in place and the doors even locked when you pushed the buttons down. "If we needed a secure place to hide in this will be great," I thought to myself, not sharing my pessimistic feelings about the outcome of the impending battle. They even had the big "Soss" Wall for Jesus sake, he will just flatten us all.

John Boland now had the binonculars and was standing on the Zephyr car roof and was excitedly scanning all around him. This was really different for him as he was used to living in a flat in London, in the middle of a concrete Jungle. "Bloody hell" he said "I hope these Geezsers are your mates, they look like bloody Indians coming down the mountain, Facks sake, this is goin' to be a right bloody punch up." I looked around at a few faces and they were not impressed with him cursing like that.

A young John Boland center and myself left on Portmarnock beach

Before we could say anything to him we spotted Derek and a young David "Daithi Laca" Madden coming through Heeney's gap next door and they had the two blond Gunning brothers with them. "Maybe we won't be needing the old wine Zephyr car to retreat to after all," I thought and smiled to myself "Things are really looking up."

The two Gunning brothers were hardy lads with Christy the older one, being as "wild as a march hare," as they say and generally up for anything. Gerard (Gerry) was the younger quieter one. These two brothers would end up being lifelong friends of mine and my brother Noel, as we grew up and became men together.

The Battle of Turnapin Lane

Christy had a big stick with him and he was bashing the long grass as he walked towards us "I'll bleedin' sort them out, where's Peter Wall, where's the big Soss," as he laid into a big bunch of purple headed thistles with his stick scattering their seeds to the wind. Christy knew Peter well, because he went to Clonshaugh school with him, along with his brother Gerard and the three Madden lads. Peter lived next door to the back shop in Clonshaugh.

A view of Clonshaugh School, built in 1939

Young John Cooley had wandered down from our house and being a quiet lad he was a bit bemused by all the wild carry on around him. Then Jimmy Heeney from next door arrived and he had Olive his sister with him. She was carrying a bottle of water and she said she would be a nurse but she wasn't going to be the only one. She disappeared and returned with a full set of battle nurses including Linda Curtis, her own sisters Mary and Theresa, Linda my sister and Veronica Pepper. Little Paul Curtis came along for few minutes but ran when it all got too noisy for him. Maybe he remembered the hole in his foot!

Chapter 10

Carmel Brudell, Hubert's older sister had arrived but she being older, maybe thirteen or so was laughing at the childish carry-on of us all. They tore up sheets to use as bandages. One of them had a red lipstick and was painting on red blood already. Linda and Carmel were dispatched up to our house to get empty glass milk bottles and fill them with water to clean the wounded during battle. Now that the girls were around we all got a little braver and louder.

"Ok lads, this is the story", I explained, trying to sound in charge. "We were watching them from the big shed earlier on and it looks like they are HQ'd up at Murphy's peacock." "What does HQ'd mean?" ask my sister Linda, "Where they're hiding, bleedin' dopey girls" Noel said gruffly. Christy interrupted, "Can we get up on the shed again for another look?" I replied "No, Ma will spot us and she will come down and scatter us." Christy replied sarcastically "Some soldier you are, afraid of your Mammy!" John Boland jokingly added "Hey mate, I'm bloody well afraid of Auntie May, she has a great left hook!"

This got a few laughs but the brother Noel wasn't impressed. He retorted with "Shut bleedin' up Gunner or I will shove that stick up," but before he could finish, a big racket of noise started coming from the enemy's HQ up at Murphy's shed. It had a corrugated roof and they had started banging it like a drum. It sounded like african tribal drums "DUM dum dum dum dum dum dum dum, DUM dum dum dum dum dum dum dum, and there was a lot of cheering as well. John Boland still had the binonculars and started counting them one by one. "One, Foo, Free, Four, Five, facking hell there's facking millions of fhem," his accent was getting a few sniggers, but at the same time he was really winding us up.

The Battle of Turnapin Lane

We had four "shields" between us, which were the lids of the small oil drums. We picked up one each, started walking a bit closer to them and started banging them in retaliation. John Boland was first out in front, adding to the din by banging one of the wooden swords we had made on his shield. Christy Gunning got really excited and jumped up and down on the roof of the Zephyr car and started banging it with his stick. Oh yes we could be noisy as well. It was now well after two o'clock and all of the noise started getting everyone excited and agitated. Derek Madden piped up, "Now hold on lads, what's the plan here, what are our tactics today? Come on back here and let's make our plan, you just can't run at them banging shields with your swords, they have arrows and sticks, we need to have a plan."

He was right, but the loud noise had unsettled us. The nurses meanwhile were all sitting around on the white car, giggling at what was going on. My sister Linda and Theresa Heeney were a bit quieter than the others, not sure of what was going to happen. Linda chewed her hair while Theresa was biting her nails as usual.

Jimmy "Skitcher" Heeney asked loudly, "Is Garter (Gerry Madden) going to be here at 3 o'clock for the back road stuff and will he have his bow and arrows?" "Yes" Derek replied, "he will whistle when he is ready to start firing." "Ok" Jimmy said, "I am with him out on the back road. I will get to Darcy's gate and with the Gatt I will scatter them with this bag of muck balls. Let them come as far as Mahony's car, its closer and I can hit that from the gate. I am going to lie low in McKenna's field, and make sure none of them are creeping down here on the back road." "Good thinking Jimmy," I added quickly "I would never had thought of that." So off Jimmy went carrying his Gatt and his ammo. This bit of planning had settled us down. He kept low as he went so as not to give his surprise attack away. As Jimmy had said we needed to get them out of the peacock and closer to us into Mahonys' car. Gerry Gunning suggested charging them first and then when they counter attacked we retreat quickly. They will have come as far as Mahony's car and settle there when we have retreated back here. "What a great idea" I said "Lets do it."

Hold on Noel Cooley shouted "there is two of them coming towards us with a white flag, it's Johnny Darcy and Noel "Hacker" Murphy, bleedin' knackers! give me an arrow over here quick!" "No No," Derek Madden shouted out "we can't do that they are under a white flag, let's go out to meet them and get the story." "I'll go" I said, " and bring Hubert with me." Hubert went white in the face and said "No way, No way, not me." I didn't blame him, it wasn't really his fight anyway. With that Gerry Gunning said he would come, so we grabbed our shields and swords and walked out to meet them at Roche's fence. Before I left I put on my blue crash helmet, now I really looked the part of a leader.

As we walked out slowly to meet them, Gerry Gunning walked beside me. I had noticed he had a slight stammer when he spoke earlier. He sounded nervous as he said to me "That Pete Wall is huge isn't he?" With my helmet on I couldn't really hear him that well, so I tilted it back off my ear. I replied "Yes he is here". Gerry replied "No, No I said he is big isn't he". " Oh yeah, he is big alright, but Gerry," as I put my hand on his shoulder "The bigger they are the harder they fall." Gerry nodded approvingly as we arrived at Roche's fence.

The Battle of Turnapin Lane

With that I came face to face with my two ex-buddies. It seemed like ages since I had seen them. Johnny stuck out his hand and I shook it. He shook Gerry Gunning's hand as well, he knew him well from Clonshaugh school. "How are we doing this?" Johnny asked, and what are the rules?" "The usual I think" I replied quickly. Not having thought about this before, we were all a little unsure of how the battle would be fought and declared won.

Noel Murphy shook our hands as well and added "I have an idea. we both have a flag each, yours at your HQ, and ours at the Peacock. Nobody holds the flag, it's on a stick, standing at both our HQ's. We try to get yours and you try to get ours."

Fair enough I thought, this sounded reasonable. Maybe, there won't be a blood bath after all. Just to be sure I asked "What about rules of combat."

"No kicking or pulling hair" Johnny suggested. "No arrows to the head, and no slings" said Noel Murphy. Gerry Gunning looked at me, but I said nothing about our plan with Jimmy Heeney. I could hear John Boland shouting in the backround "Cham' on lads, lets get it started, lets bloody murder them!" I smiled and added, "They're bleedin' mad, aren't they?" which got no reaction at all. Moving on quickly I added, "Only a Turnapin Lane man can lift the flag." This took Pete Wall out of the equation, "other than that, it's anything goes." "Fair enough," we all said, shook hands and walked away. Johnny and Noel were cold and I smelt a rat.

As we turned away and still under the white flag the drums started up again. With that arrows were now starting to whizz past us. Gerry Gunning got one in the back and one hopped of my helmet

Chapter 10

so we started running to get out of range but we were still too close. There was at least three of them already hiding in Mahony's car and they were firing the arrows at us one after the other. "No need for the false charge to get them into the car now," I shouted to Gerry Gunning as we ran back together. As I charged back through the long grass I didn't spot the rusty wire fence and I duly fell over. There was a big cheer from Mahony's car as I did so. I scrambled to my feet and got another arrow to my back. Another cheer went up. As I got up I noticed I had cut my shin really badly and I was bleeding, great I thought, a war wound already and we hadn't even started!

Gerry Gunning fell over grass clumps, cutting his hand in the blind panic of retreat. The previous evening they had tied the stumps of long grass together to create traps and they were working. The battle had started 15 minutes early and Jimmy Heeney needed to know about capturing the flag. Back at HQ I had to shout to stop everyone just running at them when they seen my bloody leg, especially John Boland and the brother Noel who were both going bananas! We cut a square white flag and with lipstick painted a red spot on it. Christy Gunning tied it to his stick and jammed it into the aerial hole on the white car. I explained that it had to be a Turnapin lane man to lift theirs and our flag. Christy wasn't impressed but he still volunteered to stand guard at our flag. I reckoned Christy staying with the flag was more to do with the girls that were gathered around the car than any bravery on his part. I was bleeding and Veronica Pepper came over and gave me a bandage. Olive Heeney had the water so she washed it for me, before Veronica wrapped the bandage around my leg. I was playing a blinder as the wounded brave leader. We regrouped for a few minutes.

The Battle of Turnapin Lane

We could see their flag sticking out of the roof of the peacock, and guess who was minding it, Oh Yes, the big "Soss" Wall. My Turnapin lane man only to capture the flag had backfired. Nobody could get past him so we needed him drawn away. Jimmy Heeney was going to be our only chance.

I asked Hubert to do the run to Jimmy Heeney out on the back road and explain to him the capturing of the flag piece. Hubert was a really fast runner and in a flash he was gone with the message, "Get to Darcy's gate, and shower Mahony's car with sling shots. Then sneak on into the end of Murphy's garden and shower the peacock with shots and drag "Soss" Wall after you. The flag sticking up on the peacock is what you need to get to."

It took us three attempts to get Hubert to remember and recite the correct message back. He was very excited. Meanwhile all of us got our bows and arrows and started advancing towards them. There was now seven of us on the battlefield. Myself, Noel, Derek & Daithi Madden, Gerry Gunning, John Boland and John Cooley. We were picking up their arrows as we went and shooting them back but we were not yet close enough to do damage. They had started banging on the top of Mahony's car and were getting fed up waiting for us. With that Jimmy Heeney had got his instructions and now in over Darcy's gate he started firing hard muck-balls and scoring direct hits on Mahony's car. Andrew Roberts got one in the hand and they were all shouting, "no slings no slings, no slings allowed." "What about the arrows in back, bleedin' cheaters," Noel Cooley shouted. After their earlier ambush of myself and Gerry Gunning, all bets were off, this was war. They bolted from the car towards Darcy's gate to get to Jimmy Heeney so we had them in open

Chapter 10

country. Derek Madden was a great shot and we launched shot after shot in on the "Top of the Lane" army.

Young John Cooley kept dropping his arrows as he was terrified. I scored a few direct hits on Eddie Madden and Thomas Whelan as they ran and jumped towards Darcy's gate, from where Jimmy Heeney was launching the muck-balls. This was doing them major damage. This slowed them up a bit but there was still seven of them heading straight for the sling toting Jimmy.

These were Johnny Darcy, Eddie Madden (wounded), Terry Deane, Noel, Dessie and Paul Murphy plus Thomas Whelan (another wounded) from Swords. Andrew Roberts stayed behind in Mahony's car. I was worried about him because as a Turnapin man, he could legally capture our flag. He was also a great runner and bigger than us.

We pinned them down for while and then Jimmy moved on and started trying to draw the "Soss" Pete Wall away from the peacock and the flag. Every time Pete ducked a muck-ball he made a run towards Jimmy. Johnny Darcy shouted "stay where you are Soss, don't move, its the flag they want." As we were firing our bows I noticed Christy Gunning had left our flag unguarded and was coming up behind us. Andrew Roberts was now the danger man.

I decided to head over to where he was in Mahony's car, but luckily he had retreated back to the peacock because his hand was cut. He had cut it on the Rusty door car frame as he tried to avoid the hail of muck balls raining in from Jimmy Heeney's sling. Their causalities were mounting up. Meanwhile at both HQ's, all the girls were jumping up and down screaming. Geraldine and Lillian

The Battle of Turnapin Lane

Murphy were jumping up and down on the peacock roof cheering on their brothers. I noticed John Boland's three sisters standing close to the peacock. They were staying in No 33 next door to Murphys. Three london girls, Tina, Jackie and little susan were standing watching a full scale battle. "Come on Johnny Boy" they shouted as their brother John got stuck in. Oh yes we were in the middle of a proper battle.

Three nurses Linda Cooley, Susan Boland, and Theresa Heeney

Chapter 10

Out of nowhere and with the battle raging I heard a sharp shrill whistle which was Gerry Madden's call to say he was on the back road ready to join the battle. He was bang on time. I looked towards the back road where he was and behind the bushes I saw a small plume of black smoke rising into the air. Then it happened. There was a terrific "Whusshe" and a long high flaming arrow flew through the air landing in the tall dry grass in directly in front us in Mahony's garden! Then there was another. "My Jesus" I shouted "What was Gerry Madden at?" There was another four to come and as they landed the petrol-soaked rags that Gerry had tied to the top of the arrows, spread fire all around in immediate vicinity of landing. Johnny Darcy ran at one, picked it up and shot it towards our end, still burning brightly as it hit Timmon's garden and exploded in flames. Gerry's last shot dropped short straight into the big hedge at Darcy's gate. In seconds it was a mass of flames. I looked around at all the fires but the one in the hedge was the biggest. The smoke from the burning grass was really thick and the hedge fire was crackling really loudly as it burned.

I shouted "Retreat, Retreat, everybody, Retreat." "What is he Jaysuz' at?" Noel shouted to me, Derek shouted "That's his secret weapon and it's no secret anymore." "Bleedin right there," I replied "Run, for Jesus sake, Run,!"

This was a classic headless chicken scene. With the gardens now on fire, the grown ups and parents were running out in force, coming from all angles. My mother had run up our garden and started giving the girls coal sacks to give to anyone who wanted them. We started to beat down the flames with streaming eyes and coughing through the smoke. Despite all this we were starting to make progress against the burning grass, but the hedge fire was still the big one. We had no hope of getting that one out ourselves.

Everyone was out now watching the spectacle unfold. I nearly died when I saw the red fire engine with the words DUBLIN FIRE BRIGADE on the side. With the siren blaring, the Fire -Engine pulled up at Darcy's gate on the back road. It looked completely out of place as it arrived. The flames in Darcy's hedge were leaping as high if not higher than the Brigade truck itself when it finally stopped beside it. Then someone shouted "Scarper!" and with that there was a mass exodus, as we all starting running towards Heeney's gap to get away from the chaotic scenes that would go down in legend as the "The Battle of Turnapin Lane". Even the dogs were running with us.

I dropped my coal bag, flung away my helmet, sword, bow and arrow and ran like the "B'Jaysus Devil." I didn't want to be a identified as a ring leader. My bandage started to unravel but I didn't care and I didn't stop for anything. I just ran and didn't stop until I was at McGuirk's river. Everyone else had the same idea. Within ten minutes everyone from both sides were at the river sitting around trying to grasp what had just happened. Gerry Madden was there and his hand had been burned by the last arrow and that's why it fell short into Darcy's big hedge. He was holding it in the cool river water for some relief and I couldn't believe he was smoking as he did so. Pete Wall came over the gate and joined us. He was wowing saying "What a deadly day that it was." Everyone had black faces with streaks from the watering eyes running down their cheeks. All the nurses were there and it looked like a scene from a war film.

Chapter 10

What remained of my bandage was black and my shin was really hurting me. Last to come was Johnny Darcy, running like the wind and panting, telling us that "Gockypoocher" was the one who had called the Fire-Brigade and said excitedly that my Ma was looking for us. "Jaysuz, we are in for it now" Noel said "don't remind me" I added, resigning myself to inevitable thumping we were going to get. Just like in 1916, the leaders would have to take the blame and pay for it with their hides.

Last to arrive was a grinning Skitcher Heeney who had been way up at the top of Murphy's garden when all hell had broken loose. He had just stayed where he was and after the big scatter he had just walked over to Murphy's peacock and took the flag off the stick. "There you are lads," as he threw down their flag for all to see, "Bottom of the Lane lads are the winners." "Not so fast" said Noel Murphy as he unfurled our flag and threw it on top on theirs. He had taken it with him as he raced towards Heeney's gap with the rest of us.

There was a silence for a few seconds until Pete Wall stood up and broke the ice "Fair play to you Skitcher, lets call it a draw!" as he stuck out his hand to shake Jimmy's and fair play to you Hacker Murphy, fair play to you all, that was the best day ever, Jayzus, can we do it all again next week?" We all looked at each other and started laughing. We were all back together again, friends together and I was really happy.

Post Script: Whenever I smell burning grass or straw I am immediately back in the middle of the Battle of Turnapin Lane.

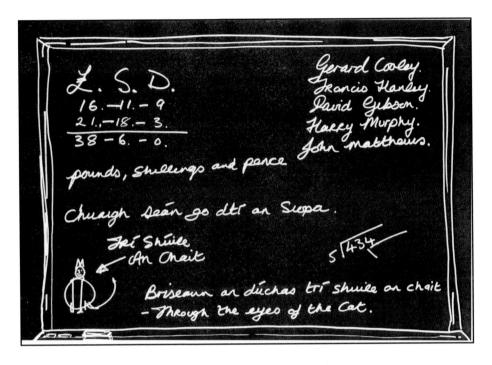

CHAPTER 11

Coming home from Larkhill School

I attended Larkhill School from 1965 to 1970 during which time I only had two teachers. My first teacher was in 1st class and he was Mr O'Donnell. Everyone called him "Smirkey" and he was the classic school teacher. Tweed jacket with the leather elbow patches, glasses under bushy eyebrows and off course, the omni present side kick of corporal punishment, namely Mr "Bata", the stick. He wasn't pleasant to me at all as he glared through his glasses at his class of over thirty students. I can still hear his stick swishing down on my young outstretched hands. Thankfully for me, within a year my second and final teacher, Mr Hardiman came along and I really liked him.

Coming home from Larkhill School

He had arrived with a new group of fresh, young-gun teachers straight from teacher's college. Among these were Mr. Moran, Mr. McCarthy, Mr .Lane and Mr. Waldron. They all looked like they belonged in a band from the fifties with their teddy boy quiffed hair styles and smart dark suits. Noel my younger brother ended up with Mr Waldron.

The head master at the time was Mr. J.J. Lawlor or "Jesse James" as he was known to us. He was a big tall man with white grey hair and he wore an old style double breasted dark navy suit with a waistcoat underneath. One afternoon I was queuing for the class allocation of rubbers, pen nibs and blotting paper in the school shop beside his office. While in this small room I heard a commotion outside his office next door. Terrified I looked out to see him giving some older lads six of the best.

They were pleading and sobbing, all at the same time, as he was slapping their hands. He wasn't holding back either. To see a man that big, striking full force, causing so much pain, really frightened the daylights out of me. Only once did I ever get slapped by him. Running in the playground after the bell was the crime. There was no discussion, nothing, he just shouted, "Hold out your hand" and whack!, I got it. His first touch as he steadied the hand gently at the tip, lulled you into a false sense of security, then the swishing of the stick as he took aim. Three slaps to each hand, Jesus it hurt. By the time the sixth slap came I was completely shattered, my two hands numb with pain.

The other older teachers there at the time were Mr Kilmartin, Mr Cleere, Mr O'Donoghue and Mr Clandillon. Mr O'Donogue looked a little bit like Inspector Poirot as he entered the school building wearing his wide legged and heavy pinstriped suit. He was a low sized man and he also wore a hat and a moustache. I know he lived closed by because he walked to school.

Chapter 11

Mr Scully was another older teacher and he ran the choir which I was a part of most of the time. We performed in the assembly hall singing songs from Gilbert & Sullivan's HMS Pinafore and the like. He was a red haired, red faced, chain smoker, a bit of a blunder-bus, but he was alright and he didn't use the stick that much.

I have many memories of Larkhill and a lot of them are combined in my next story. It is set in the year 1970 when I was in sixth class and within weeks of this journey back to my home in Turnapin, I would be leaving Larkhill to attend secondary school in Belcamp College. I enjoyed my years in Larkhill School because it was a place where I was really good at something and I had my reports to prove it.

It was a Thursday afternoon and I was standing at the bus stop in front of house No 227 on the main Swords road in Larkhill. As I sat on the wall of 227, I found myself looking in at no 229 next door, which was on down a little ways towards the shops and I wondered why that particular house was always so badly kept. After a few minutes some one from 227 walked out through the front door so I duly moved away from their low front wall to stand beside the bus-stop standing out on the path near the road. There was no bus shelter there at this time.

I was watching the passing traffic trying to spot one of my four Cooley uncles who drove taxis' so I could get a lift home with them and save my bus fare for the next day. They would be usually empty as they returned after getting a job into Dublin from the airport. These were my father's brothers, Willie, John, Tom and Joseph. Along with my father Gerard, these five brothers were known all over Dublin and to this day I still meet people who tell about their exploits. Hard working, old school and well respected are the comments I hear mostly. They were coal merchants in winter and taxi men in the summer.

Coming home from Larkhill School

The big boss, my grandfather Bill, drove a taxi in the summertime as well but he didn't stop for us at the school bus stop. He probably thought it was too dangerous of a place to stop and he was right. On at least one occasion someone was knocked down and killed at our bus-stop.

The Cooley's : L to R, John, Gerard, Willie, Bill and Tom

Chapter 11

I thought about what my saved bus fare would get me the next morning. Tomorrow was Friday morning and it was chewing gum card day. I would get off the bus at the Brookville Chemist, walk around past Moores' and on into Finnerans for my penny bars. Donohoes was two shops down from Finnerans on the left, past Murrays the chemist, but old Mr Donohue, in his snow white shop coat, never stocked any of the chewing gum cards, so Finnerans was always the place to go.

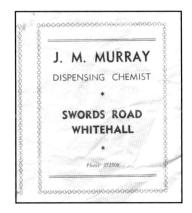

Each week day morning heading out to school I would normally get a sixpence or "a Tanner" as we called it. "Tuppence up, Tuppence back, and Tuppence to spend" that was the six pennies in total.

On Fridays however, as it was escape day and chewing gum card day, Da gave us a full shilling (12 pennies) each. The cards were 3d (old money) for a set. Back then there was such a coin as a three penny piece and just to make it awkward there were two types of threepenny pieces (Truppence). One was the Irish one, a small silver coin with a harp on one side and a rabbit on the other, while the English coin, which was still legal currency here, was a big brass coloured chunky coin with a castle draw-bridge on the front and the Queen's head on the back.

We also had English pennies, sixpences, shillings and two shilling piec-es to deal with as well. When Decimalisation happened in 1971 this put an end to all this mixed up coinage. The first time I saw the new money was in King's shop in Santry. I was with Dominick Duffy and I changed a shilling which had become 5 new pence. I got three new pence as change and I gave one new penny to my uncle Dominick to inspect. Everyone was intrigued by this new, shiney, smaller coinage. I was a bit miffed when Dominick never gave it back to me. The big sensation of the new coins however, was the new 50p piece. This was replacing the old "Ten bob" note and people were really sad to see this old faithful go.

The friday school shilling got us two sets of cards plus two penny bars, happy days, everyone loved Fridays. There were lots of different types of cards and I collected all of them.

Chapter 11

Old Mr Finneran, a balding red faced man who wore a wine full sleeved cardigan did well to keep us going with packs of cards on the mad morning card rush. The buzz in the school yard for swaps on Fridays was absolutely manic. Looking back I reckon the chewing gum itself was giving us the rush. This was white or pink and was very sweet. The more you chewed it the tougher it got!

The High Chaparall cards were the very latest. This was an American cowboy series that ran from 1967 to 1971 and we watched it on our new Bush colour television set. This was rented from RTV rentals in Northside shopping centre and when it broke down, Tommy "Crazy Prices" Tyrell was always parachuted in to fix it. Tommy used to work in Bush before going to work as a taxi man operating out of Dublin airport.

We would all sit around the broken television waiting for "God" to arrive. Ma was always glad to see Tommy arrive to save her, especially during winter time when she couldn't run us out of the house to play.

The High Chaparall show had a great theme tune and Big John Cannon was the main man. His wife was called Victoria and I seem to remember she was Mexican and she shouted a lot. She had a brother called Monalito who grinned a lot and there was Big John's son called Billy Blue boy who cried a lot! How my father would laugh when he saw Blue boy curling his lip all the time with his blue eyes filling up with tears. Once he had killed an "Injun" and was having a hard time "dealing" with it. Oh yes, a cowboy with a conscience. Only the yanks can do that stuff.

These weren't the first chewing gum cards, oh no, we were seasoned collectors by now. Earlier card fads were The Man from Uncle, Batman and Robin, English team Football cards and way back, maybe the very first for me, there were the American Civil War cards.

Chapter 11

The American Civil War cards were in glorious colour and the scenes were really gory with blood, guts and cannon balls flying in all directions. Each card had it's very own title. "Pushed to his Doom" was one I recall showing an unfortunate union soldier being pushed by a "Johnny Reb" onto some very sharp spikes. Another one was "Crushed by the Wheels" where an injured "Johnny Reb" lay screaming and terrified as he is about to be crushed by the wheel of a speeding union cannon gun. All around the battlefield sharp bayonets were plunging into unfortunate soldiers with eye bulging pain for us to enjoy.

Meanwhile back at the bus-stop I was excited anyway because I had my summer report in my bag and I had just managed to get 3rd place in the class from my master, Mr Hardiman. He was always organising something and when he got stressed, especially during issuing of "The Lark," the fags would come out because he really enjoyed his cigarettes. Mr O'Brien had started it but everyone got involved near publication time. Mr Hardiman would have us putting the coloured paper pages in sequence and then stapling them together. Looking back at them now the graphics were very basic.

Da and Ma were very proud of me doing well in school. They liked Mr Hardiman and he was a great teacher to me. I loved his afternoon story readings from Ali Ba Ba and the Forty Thieves. Daydreaming heaven.

Coming 3rd in the class wasn't so bad, Christopher Philpot and Philip Byrne had beaten me to 1st and 2nd, this time, a come-back for them from last year when I got the No 1 spot. This was important to me because I wanted to be in the "A" class in my new school. I was sad that I was leaving three weeks later because my primary school days were just about over. Belcamp College was beckoning and I was going to really miss Mr. Hardiman and my Larkhill classmates.

Coming home from Larkhill School

In a curious twist, I didn't have any school friends in my Larkhill class from Turnapin Lane. The nearest I had was Francis Hanley in Santry village as well as Barney Finnegan from Collinstown lane . All my playground buddies like John Daly, John Matthews, David Gibson, Alex Farrell, Christy Dowler, Andrew Gibney, Peter Shields, Denis Mcnamara and Harry Murphy were all from around the Beaumont and Larkhill area.

John Matthews lived up past Kitty's shop, where I used to buy my american calvary soldiers and my Stanley Gibbons stamps.

These soldiers lived in forts made by myself out of flat lolipops sticks that I found on the path kerbs by the road sides around the shops. I once brought John out to Turnapin Lane and we went across to the Pipers Hole pond in William's field to get a dog's skull that I knew was there and because he was into that sort of thing.

I knew it was Rex Heeney's skull because my father had shot him, along with our own dog Rory as they swam in the pond. They had been out worrying/killing sheep the previous night. It was cruel, but that was his answer to the problem at that time, he often talks about it now, regretting what he did. John Matthews gave me a real feathered arrow for the skull.

868	8	Proinnsias ó hAinle	
876	9	Pól ó Dálaigh	
878	0	Gearóid ó Cúile	
883	1	Pádraig Mac Amhlaoidh	

Larkhill 4th Class Photograph (1968) Names not complete

Gerard Cooley, Francis Hanley, Denis McNamara,Stephen Stears, 2nd,3rd,4th,5th in from Left. Harry Murphy peeping,Sam Carroll left at back, 4th Left at back Christy Dowler, moving right, Bernard Finnegan, Joe Donnell, Brian Bone, Ernie Saputo, Peter Cox. Front center, Peader Hardiman, to his right Chistopher Philpot, James O'Malley, David Gibson, John Massey, Martin Goodman, behind him, Anthony Rock..

207

scoil náisiúnta				Scoil an Le
1/7/68		618	1	Stiofán Stears
1/7/68		717	2	Andrias ó Gilne
1/7/68		597	3	Caoimhín de Róiste
1/7/68		650	4	Peadar Cox
1/7/68		658	5	Ernesto Saputo
1/7/68		120	6	Caoimhín ó Maitiú
1/7/68		652	7	Seán ó Dálaigh
1/7/68		662	8	Bearnáid ó Fionnagáin
1/7/68		823	9	Derc ó Riain
1/7/68		831	0	Máirtín ó Godáin
1/7/68		835	1	Brian de Bothún
1/7/68		846	2	Fraolach Mausberry
1/7/68		847	3	Mioclás Mac Cata
1/7/68		856	4	Seosamh ó Domhnaill
1/7/68		857	5	Alastar ó Fearghail
1/7/68		862	6	Donncadha Mac Conmara
1/7/68		864	7	Toirdhealbhach Mac Thbeartaí
1/7/68		868	8	Proinnsias ó hAingle
1/7/68		876	9	Pól ó Dálaigh
1/7/68	29/6/51	878	0	Gearóid ó Cuile
1/7/68		883	1	Pádraig Mac Amhlaoidh
1/7/68		731	2	Seán ó h Iotaird
1/7/68		886	3	Aithí Gibson

Date		Number		Name
1/7/68		746	4	Antoine Rock
1/7/68		748	5	Proinnsias Dalaruh
1/7/68		767	6	Annraí, ó Murchú
1/7/68		887	7	Caoimhín ó Fionnagáin
1/7/68		783	8	Pádraig ó Siothail
1/7/68		762	9	Roibeard ó Miocháin
1/7/68		117	0	Peadar ó Maoileoin
1/7/68		942	1	Criostóir Philpott
1/7/68		932	2	Pilib ó Broin
1/7/68		923	3	Seán ó Massaí
1/7/68		958	4	Criostóir ó Duinn
1/7/68		926	5	Pádraig Ó Uill
1/7/68		858	6	Seán ó Maitiú
1/7/68		324	7	Sam ó Cearbhaill
1/7/68		176	8	Séamuis ó Máille
1/7/68		578	9	Antoine ó h Eilgéis
1/7/68		667	0	Tomás ó Donnchutaigh
1/7/68		581	1	Mícheál ó Clintiún
1/7/68		556	2	Breandán Mac Cába
1/7/68		731	3	Seán ó h Iobáird
1/11/68		747	4	Daithí ó Ruanaí
23/7/69		582	5	Daithí ó Muirí

Iomlán na ndaltaí ar Rollaí ar an teastanac seo g...

...ntear anseo ar an gcéad lá den scoilbliain. I. Uimir na ndaltaí ar Rolla...

Coming home from Larkhill School

Above : Statue of Mary in Main corridor

Below : Toilets and cloakroom

Larkhill 2011

Chapter 11

Larkhill Staff 1970
B. Row L-R: J. Cleere, T. Walsh, M. Kilmartin, P. Kennedy, T. Quinn, B. Moran
M.Row L-R: L. Morrissey, R. Waldron, J. Gleeson, T. McCarthy, J. Barrett,
A. Lane, P. Hardiman, C. O'Brien.
F. Row L-R: J. Scully, P. Sexton, T. O'Donnell, M. O'Driscoll, J.J. Lalor (P).
G. Mullery, C. Clandillon, F. O'Donoghue

SCHOOL SPORTS 1968	:		
9 Three Legged	(2 (3	Dan McLoughlin & Stephen Pepper Denis Murphy & Thomas Rossiter	(4) (4)

JUNIOR PAGE

A: OPTICAL ILLUSION by Joseph Casey.

One day my mammy said that she would visit a friend who lived in Ballymun flats. As our friend lived at the top of an eight storey building we had to climb a lot of stairs. When we reached the top my mammy went into the flat. She said I could stay outside for a while. I looked over the railings and saw a sixpence, as I thought, at the bottom. As I went down two flights of stairs it became bigger and as I reached the bottom I found, to my disappointment, that it was not a sixpenny piece but the lid of a dustbin.

@ @ @ @ J @ @ @ @ @ @ @ @ @ @ @ @

DREAMS COME TRUE   by Brian Donohue.

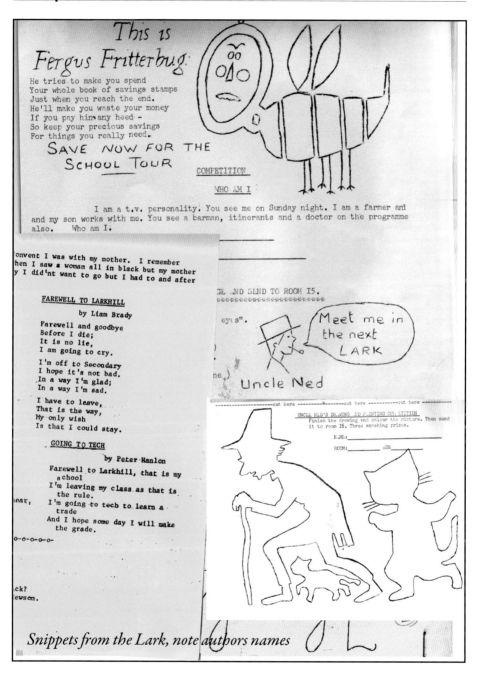

Snippets from the Lark, note authors names

Coming home from Larkhill School

Meanwhile back at the bus-stop, my younger brother Noel had just arrived after school detention for messing in class. "What kept you?" I asked, "Waldron kept us all back to do lines, I must not bleedin' talk while teacher is out of the room, fifty lines each, the bleedin eejit, I wasn't even there, I was down in the jacks." He flung his school bag back against the small frontwall of 227 and then he joined me at the bus stop. He started watching the road with me. He pretended to see someone saying "Here he isn't, No, not him, no wait, no not him again," and so on as he pointed at the passing cars. Noel was only 11 months younger than me, and he was lucky because he had a buddy from Turnapin Lane in his class in Larker. His name was John Connolly and he lived in No 25 Turnapin lane. Noel wouldn't have me to "mind" him next year, so I was glad he and John could travel together.

" Here's Da, look , look!" Noel shouted excitedly and started waving at him in his grey and white Ford Consul. It looked like Da had a fare, so we got a wave, a smile and a flash of the lights as he sped past. Then it was back to the watching and waiting again.

Ford Consul similar to Da's Taxi

Chapter 11

I was wondering had Da managed to get me the Peter Shilton World Cup Esso medal that I needed to finish my full set of 30. I had brought a few Mike Summerbees and Bobby Charltons in to school last week to get a swap just in case, but no joy, Peter Shilton was the hardest to get.

There was great excitment because this coming Sunday, England and Germany were playing in the quarter final of the 1970 world cup. This was going to be a rematch of the 1966 World Cup Final and I would be cheering for England. Earlier in the year, Dana had won the Eurovision and her song "All kinds of everything" got to No.1 in the english charts. I reckoned that if they liked our song that much, I could like their football team. Back then I was a Manchester United fan and I had met all the 1968 European Cup winning team at Dublin airport and got most of their authographs including Matt Busbys' their famous manager. As usual George Best was no where to be seen. More importantly however, Dubliner Tony Dunne was playing for United at the time and I managed to get his autograph as well. By the time Tony finished playing for United in the early 70's he had made over 500 appearances for them.

Manchester United 1968 team, Tony Dunne, middle row 2nd from left

Back at the bus stop, the No.16 bus came and went but this was no use to us as it turned left up Shanowen Road. Noel was getting impatient. "I'm starving" Noel whined as he spun around the bus stop swinging one arm out into the path of the oncoming traffic. "Jesus be careful, Noel" I shouted, "you just missed that old man there on the bike." "What man?" he answered, "Oh him, I don't care, I'm starvin." he added nonchantly.

Just then the old familiar 41A bus appeared on the incoming bend facing Molloy's dentist on the far side of the road and we were saved from Noel's stomach rumblings. The bus stopped and on we jumped. Joe the

Chapter 11

bus conductor was standing there, beside the bell, smiling and munching on his chewing gum. We stayed downstairs and made our way up to the "Television" seats up at the front. We sat under the advert for "Granby" sausages and we now had to look at all the faces looking up at us. I was not a great bus traveller so I had to focus. I tried not to look out at the moving buildings as this would make me travel sick.

Being a bit shy back then, I could not stare straight ahead into twenty sets of onlooking eyes so I turned to look out the side windows as we drove towards Santry. On the left I saw the Hostess shop move by, next the Comet pub and then Gormley's butchers shop. Next I spotted Mr. Tobin brushing the front pathway outside his shop.

No one ever seemed to go into Tobins. For us this was mainly due to the fact that his shop was last on the going home side and as our money was spent on the way into school, there was none left for Joe. Honest Joe Tobin he was known as, he didn't discriminate, he overcharged everybody! He always reminded me of a cat watching a mouse when us school children entered his shop. He would stand and seemed to "Hovver" and this unnerved us. I think he had a bad experience of children stealing from him. Now would we!

He was one of the original traders in the area and when he came to Larkhill first he had a shop across the road where Peter's Chipper is now. Mr Tobins first shop was called the Brookville Stores.

Passing the turn at Shanowen Road we drove on past McCairn's Motors on the left. There I spotted rows of new Bedford P&T (Post Office) trucks, sitting like big white and orange "Dinky Toys" on the forecourt, all new and clean, ready for delivery. Joe the bus conductor made his rounds with the ticket machine and what a lovely sound he made. As he came towards us Noel was rummaging in his pockets for his two pennies. "Have you got them?" I asked him quietly, "No, I thought I had them, no wait, I think they are in my pencil case." Joe smiled as he expected the usual "lost me bus fare story" but then quick as a flash Noel found them and proudly put them straight into Joe's money bag. A quick wind up on the handle, ticket popped out, then pull and tear, a whirl then a jingle as my two pennies hit the leather bag as well.

Passing through Santry village itself, I saw Magenta Crescent on the right with the Garda station sitting right nextdoor to No 1, Harris's house on the corner. The station looked like something from Trumpton. Next Eugene O'Reilly's public house came into view. My fathers "second home" as my mother never got tired of saying.

Santry, Eugene O'Reilly's bar on the left now the Swiss Cottage

Then came King's Shop run by two brothers Gerry and Peter. They had recently added a Spar supermarket building beside the old shop and this is where I got Bridie Flood's Woodbine cigarettes.

Chapter 11

Bridie Flood lived in No 36 Turnapin Lane, with her mother and her married sister Eileen. Bridie regularly collared me at the top of the Lane, asking me in her gruff gravelly voice "Gerard, you wouldn't run up to Kings for me, would you, now there's a good chap, you're a topper, you are a little star." I always went for her. Eileen's husband Anthony and young Anthony their son lived there as well.

Eileen and Bridie Flood pictured in 2004

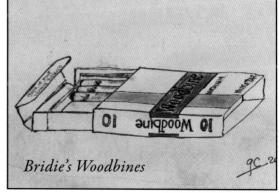

Bridie's Woodbines

Coming home from Larkhill School

When the bus stopped at the Santry Avenue lights, I saw an empty dusty space where the Forge used to be. I missed seeing the old quaint building and I'd been told that it had burnt down. I wanted to believe that they wouldn't have deliberately knocked something as pretty as that down, but they did. Things were starting to change in Santry.

View of Old Forge in Santry, taken in the late 60's

Switching sides I spotted a few big green and yellow combine harvesters, looking like big dinosaurs grazing in the fields around Savilles' on the corner of Santry avenue. Opposite Savilles' was Santry's post office which was in a lovely little Swiss styled cottage and run by the Lawless family.

On the bus Noel was starting to get giddy beside me. "What's the joke?" I asked him. He held up his hand to cover his mouth whispering, "Fish eyes" to me softly, through the laughter. He had just spotted a woman in a big green hat wearing pink "fish eye" glasses, just like the ones my sister Linda wore. This woman was staring ahead

Chapter 11

looking through us, but there was nowhere to hide in the television seat. I was now getting the bug, I started giggling, going red, hitting Noel trying to divert attention as we were now both in convulsions. The onlookers were not impressed with us.

"No manners" I heard one woman say. "God help us" replied the woman in the green hat. In the end I pulled a copy book out of my bag, so I could pretend to read it, or use it as a shield at least. The bus was now hurtling along passing Santry Woods and J.F.Kennedy Stadium on our left and then we stopped outside Lamberts at the bottom of the Barrack Hill. I could smell the wild garlic from Santry Woods. Noel really made a meal of it pinching his nose. Thankfully the woman with the glasses got off, she lived either on the main road or in Santry Close. Now we headed up the hill past Rolon Caravans and Murphy's Furry Park pitch and putt course. As we passed, I felt over my left eye as I remembered a sickening "thud" on the bone there. Only a few weeks earlier Noel Murphy had split me open as he swung his putter on the 1st tee box acting the maggot, I had to get stitched in Temple Street, he thought it was hilarious.

Now nearing home, Noel jumped up and rang the bell twice. Joe the bus conductor already knew we were getting off as he was on our route most days. Off we jumped and as I did, the smell of the engine fumes gave my stomach a little churn as they smothered me in it's "pull away" revs. I gasped for a breath of fresh air as I gave a good look around, grabbed Noel and ran across the road.

After running across the busy road, we stopped and had a "nosey" around Carley's big gates. The big concrete balls on each of the 4 pillars always impressed me, the entrance looked like the gates to a big castle.

Coming home from Larkhill School

Woodford Cottage known locally as Carley's lodge

  I hadn't noticed a woman getting off the bus behind us, she was slower than us, but she caught up with us as the gate. A tall thin woman, she walked into the entrance but took a sharp right in behind Carley's Lodge. We decided that a few bamboo sticks would do us for fishing rods to catch pinkeens with, so we followed her on into the entrance as well. I heard some women talking, "There you are Bridie, I see you're hard at it, great drying out today." "Oh there you are Sissy," Bridie, the woman in the Lodge replied "I see you have a few messages, good job you have a basket on the bike." " Yes, be-god, you're right there Bridie, I better get on, or Jack will be giving out about the dinner being late." Sissy Fizsimons was my grand aunt, my grandmother Cathy's sister and with a wave and a quick "there you are lads" she was gone. Riding slowly away from the small "bicycle depot" on her lady "high nellie" bicycle.

Chapter 11

Bridie who lived in Woodford Lodge allowed people who had to cycle to the bus corner from way down the back road in Clonshaugh, to leave their bicycles under her back window while they headed on into town (Dublin) on the bus. I thought to myself, I would be seeing a lot more of Sissy as I would be visiting her house to call for my cousin Tommy, who lived with Sissy, as he was already attending Belcamp College.

We headed up Carley's entrance for a few minutes to get bamboo sticks. Just as we left the gateway and with our few bamboos in our hands, Da came around the corner in his grey and white taxi. He was cutting back for dinner after his last job to the airport. I waved him on, but I could see he was not impressed with us taking the bamboo's out of Carleys. One of his sayings came to mind. "If you are up to some-thing, or doing some-thing you shouldn't be, I will turn up, nothing surer." Da stopped the car and Noel jumped in. I held back, as Noel threw me his bamboo sticks to carry home. I flung Noel my school bag and it landed on the back seat, then they sped off, Da blowing the horn, and Noel making faces at me through the back window. *Aunt Sissy*

Coming home from Larkhill School

Alone now, I walked down the quiet country road that led to Turnapin lane. The road banks were high with weeds like "Devil's spit", "Piss the beds" and Nettles. The air was heavy with summer smells and buzzing flies. I passed one of Carley's trees on the left where myself, Noel and my cousin Hubert Brudell had carved our names the previous summer. I remembered the day I was carving the N, in Noel's initials. I was hanging nearly upside down from a nearby branch and watching out for Tom Carley as well. It was only when I got down to the road did I notice I had done the "N" arseways. Afterwards, I blamed Noel if anyone ever spotted it.

I crossed the road to the right towards Geraghty's big tree leaving Carley's green wooden backyard gate on the left. This green gate led into Carley's farm-yard on my left. The orchard wall loomed large in the distance and inside this wall roamed "Coalie" Carley, a large vicious light brown curly guard dog that would "ate you" if he got you. He was our No 1 enemy when Carley's Orchard was to be robbed. Tom Carley was always pottering about in the orchard and the glass houses. He was a gentle and solemn character who spoke in a slow quiet way and never got out of his overalls.

Chapter 11

Tom Carley tending his plants in their concrete pots in the orchard

As I walked past Geraghty's big tree, I noticed the path was getting smaller around the base of the tree as it was growing bigger and bigger. I had to step off the path to go around it. I poked the mud walls of Geraghy's slaughter house with one of the bamboo sticks and it made a mark in the walls because they were very old and crumbling. Peering in through the windows I saw the implements that were used to butcher the unfortunate cows. I thought I saw blood dripping from an animal skin, I stepped back feeling very unnerved and hurried on my way. I saw two women coming towards me. One large, one small, one wearing a headscarf, the other much bigger woman wasn't, and both were in deep conversation.

As they got closer, the smaller one, Lizzie Hynes asked me "There you are Gerard, has the bus gone long?", " No Lizzie" I replied "Maybe about ten minutes," "Come on Betty " she said to Mrs Roberts, "We better lift our legs, that bus will be heading back from the airport by now, come on are you right, lift those feet and shift your big arse Betty, or we are going to miss the feckin' bus"! The two women rushed past me laughing as they went.

Coming home from Larkhill School

Lizzie had a crinkly face that lit up when she smiled. She kept a goat out the back of her house in No.24, her very own lawnmower. She was the driving force behind the annual Turnapin Residents "outing," which always went to Germaines in Baltinglass. Lizzie looked after us children as well and the "Gaels of Laughter" with Maureen Potter was a regular. I remember her once getting very annoyed with someone in Turnapin who had held onto the "communal" ladder for too long. This was a big news story in my Turnapin Lane.

Turnapin outing group early 1970's
B. Row L-R, Woman?, May Farrell, Gerry & Dolly Madden, Woman?,
Cathleen Timmons, Molly Roberts, Kit Finn, Joey Madden, Ethel Doran,
Neddy Madden, Jerry & Pauline Heeney, Ned Madden, Jimmy Heeney.
F. Row L-R, Har Roberts, Michael Moore, Andrew & Jimmy Roberts, Doc
Roche, Pauline Caul.

Chapter 11

Lizzie had a brother called Tommy who worked in Geraghty's slaughter house, God help him. He drove a motor bike of sorts, maybe one of them pedal to start jobs and he wasn't as friendly as Lizzie. On down the road I passed the gate on the left into the long back garden of Dunnes, No.1 Turnapin Lane. This gate was at the ditch where you could get into Carley's field. If Ma was baking apple tarts she would need cooking apples, so maybe there was to be a raid to be planned on Carley's Orchard tonight. Tom Carley sold the apples for little or nothing, but that wasn't the point, where was the fun in that? I walked around Dunne's corner, still clutching my few bamboo sticks and thankfully I was just about home.

A smiling Lizzie Hynes out gardening in the back garden of no 24, see Hillfarm House in the distance behind her

MASSEY
FERGUSON 135

CHAPTER 12

Going to work for P.J. Jones

Going to work on Jone's Farm was very much a rite of passage for all the young lads of Turnapin Lane. It was usually during the secondary school summer holidays, but sometimes there was some evening winter work available, especially coming up to Christmas when there was with a huge demand for Brussell sprouts. A few Turnapin lane men like Ned Farrell and his brother Johnny were employed full time by P.J. Jones. Johnny was a tall skinny man, just like a potato stalk, so we called him "Stalkey". He sometimes wore a soft cap. His brother Ned was called the "Duke" because he looked like P.J. Duke the famous Cavan gaelic footballer. Ned was a founder member of the local Starlights GAA team.

Going to work for P.J. Jones

Both of these men were the classic Irish bachelors, who lived only three miles from the G.P.O. but looked and sounded like they came from the heart of the west of Ireland. They lived in No 19, just two doors from me. There were two other older local lads, Jerry Heeney and Gerry Madden who were also employed full time on Jones' farm.

This small group of full time workers drove the tractors that pulled the trailers, the cabbage planting machines, the ploughs, the potato harvester and all the other mechanical gizmos that were required to keep a farm ticking over. In early spring time all of these would be engaged in getting the soil ready for the planting that would take place throughout spring and summer. Once the summer came and the ground was bursting with the first crop of vegetables, the cannon fodder labour was called in and that was us.

Back then P.J. Jones' farm was approx 100 acres and it was all in tillage, i.e under crops. The farm is still there to this day, down the back road in Clonshaugh on the way to the Baskin Cottages. He purchased the farm from the Wilson family in the late 1950's but only came to live there in 1961. Edenville is the name of the farm and today it's a little smaller than when I worked there because the M1 Motorway took away the four back fields in the 1980's. P.J. himself is from a big farming family who were involved in "contract" farming around North County Dublin. In later years he moved across the road onto land once owned by Lightfoots.

Thirteen or fourteen was usually the starting age in Jones and the ritual of "asking for a start" was around June, just as secondary school holidays were looming. My first season was in the summer of 1970 and I did four seasons there in all, up to the summer of 1973, the year I finished my Intermediate Certificate. I was technically finished primary school in 1970 so I just told a white lie about my age. The word was sent into my mother

Chapter 12

that P.J. needed a few lads to do a bit of weeding in the drills so Johnny Farrell left word that Mr Jones wanted us to drop down to see him. The talking was something you had to do personally, no around the houses on this one, you had to go down, knock on the door and talk to him directly. I suppose this was my very first job interview.

If you had been there the previous summer and didn't behave yourself, you would get a reminder from P.J. and you may not be taken back. To be honest very few were ever not taken back.

My memory of my first interview was interupting him during his lunch and waiting nervously as his wife, Theresa answered the back door. It was all a bit noisy with the young Jones children, Kenneth, David and Barbara running around the place. Baby Joseph would arrive later. When P.J. eventually appeared, he seemed a little miffed that I had interupted his lunch. He was very officious with me as he wiped away his lunch from his mouth. He asked me my name and my age. I remember saying something about pulling bulky-shank (Ragworth) weeds for Willie Snow and Stephen Fowler the previous summer to give him the impression I had loads of experience in the weed pulling game.

Knowing Johnny Farrell helped of course and the fact my grand aunt Sissy Fitzsimons lived down the road from him did me no harm either, as I stuttered my way through my introductions. My brother Noel was with me and Johnny Darcy was there as well. Derek Madden had already started a week earlier, with Gerry his older brother getting him his start. Mr Jones said "Yes," and we were all to start the following Monday morning, eight o'clock, bright and early. I was thrilled.

Our small coal yard went completely dead in the summer and I was really at my happiest when I was outdoors. I was delighted that me and

231

Going to work for P.J.Jones

my friends were all going to be working together. The few bob would be great as well. I was starting secondary school in Belcamp College the coming September and my red and yellow painted "Q Bike" would not be making the two mile trip there from Turnapin Lane. It just wasn't cool enough. I had my heart already set on a Raleigh Chopper, which were just new into Dublin bicycle shops. One of the lads in my class in Larkhill had come into to school on a beautiful red one and it really looked the business.

On our first day we all walked together from Turnapin to Jones' farm. Noel Murphy joined the crew as we headed down our garden, out through Heeney's gap, past the sewerage pumping station, then out on to the back road. That first day I remember my brother Noel and me were wearing buttoned short sleeved shirts with ship's anchors on them. His was red and mine was blue. We had small "Pork Pie" straw hats to

Chapter 12

keep the sun off us as sunburn was an occupational hazard, especially on our heads. I had told Mr Jones that I was fourteen and Noel was thirteen. We were now working full time, oh yes we were men. Walking on along the back road we passed Currans on the left, then on down to the corner at Madden's giving Derek a shout as we passed. Gerry Madden, Derek's older brother, walked with us during our first season, but the following year he would join Jerry Heeney as a biker when he bought a Honda 100 motorbike. He was always late despite having that motorbike. At least when he was walking with us we dragged him along and got him there on time. Jerry Heeney's motorbike was a wine coloured Yamaha and he lived next door to me in no 20. When I was getting a lift with him, I would sit on his bike outside his front window and wait for him to finish his breakfast. With seven younger brothers and sisters I always had company while I waited, as they stuck their heads out the window asking me "What was I doin' sitting on their brother's motorbike?"

A young Jerry Heeney on his motorbike with Dunne's corner behind him

Going to work for P.J. Jones

When he gave me a lift to Jones he absolutely terrified me and I am sure he did it on purpose. He got great delight seeing my white face as I dismounted in the small green road shed in Jones' after speeding along the twisting and turning back road with me hanging on to his heavy overcoat for dear life. Jerry always had long hair so as well as being ill with fright I was blinded with his hair blowing back into my eyes. Talk about pre morning stress before starting work!

Road shed in Jone's Yard

On this, our very first morning's trek, we passed Madden's and McGuirk's corner, getting over the gate into Barney Boland's field, crossing that familar spot at McGuirk's river as we went. Out into Collin's field we walked along the headland, up into the corner and climbed down into the ditch. Later in the summer when Collin's ploughed this field we found clay pipes and earthen jars just lying in the soil.

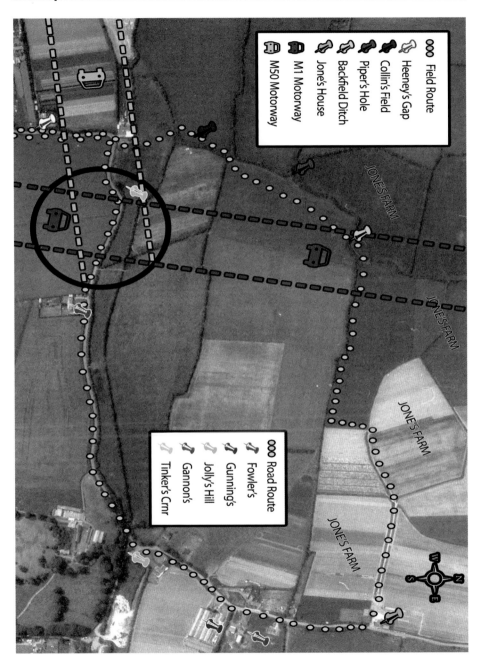

Going to work for P.J.Jones

When we emerged out of the ditch we were now in Williams' field which was huge compared to all the others. We walked diagonally across this field passing "Pipers' Hole" on our left. This field was in full meadow in early summer, so as we walked we made our trail, which we would follow back and forth for the whole summer. This flattening of a trail through this field was very important, because if and when it rained, at least we would not get our legs wet walking in the high grass.

At the top end of Williams field we crossed down through a ditch and emerged in Jones' back field. When there we walked on for another 10 minutes up along a few field headlands and into the main lane and on up to the big green shed in the yard beside where the house was. The complete journey would take us at least half an hour. All the Turnapin lads were great workers and the full crew as I remember it was. Myself, Noel Cooley, Johnny Darcy, Noel Murphy, Derek Madden, Jerry Heeney, Gerry Madden, Tommy Kavanagh, Oliver Burke, Johnny Farrell and of course the man himself, P.J Jones. Ned, Johnny's brother didn't work for P.J. until the mid 1970's.

P.J. Jones was the hands on type and every morning he was there, giving us our orders and explaining what needed to be done. With tractors and trailers loaded we then headed off to the various fields. He wasn't a very tall man and he wore a cap all of the time. In general he was good natured and friendly. He treated us fairly and with respect and everyday he worked very hard on the farm along with the rest of us.

Weeding was our first job and the fields containing the drills with the early cabbage and cauliflowers were ours. This had to be done by hand as P.J. did not like using chemicals to control the weeds once the plants were in the ground. The cabbage drills were first and P.J. gathered up a half dozen crew and started us on six drills at a time. He always gave us a demonstration of how he wanted things done. He would stay with us for an hour or so, making sure that we weren't pulling up the cabbage plants along with the weeds.

Once we finished one drill, we came to the headland and then just turned and started a new drill in the opposite direction. Some drills had more weeds than others so there was an incentive to finish yours first as you got first pick of the next six. If someone was falling behind, P.J. would jump in on the drill and bring him level with the others. This was back breaking work and you knelt to one side of the drill in the furrow as you moved along, throwing the weeds behind you. When P.J. wasn't around the messing would start. Flinging the weeds back into the face of your nearest comrade was first. Anything to ease the boredom.

Johnny Farrell was sometimes left to weed with us, a sort of a prefect or supervisor, if you like. He had a really dry sense of humour and when we were messing he would stand up slowly and say, while pretending to be talking to Mr Jones, "Pee Jay, the lads are all messin and lyin' down in the drills and they won't do any work a-tall, and Pee Jay, Jerry Heeney got sick and vomitted up flem' and everything." These words were delivered in a very slow deadpan voice with a half a smile on his face. He always made me laugh with this one.

Johnny Farrell, with cloth cap has a chat with the Gunning's

Going to work for P.J. Jones

Once we were weeding the drills of carrots and because the foliage of a carrot is like a weed itself, a lot of the carrots were pulled and lost. P.J. had an absolute fit. I don't think he planted carrots again. Lunch time came at 1 o'clock and for this we got a full hour. In the absence of watches we relied on the church bells to at least give us a noon time check. Us Turnapin lads galloped home for lunch through the fields and poached eggs on toast with beans was the usual fare. I loved when Ma had it waiting for us, but sometimes we had to cook it ourselves if she was in town. Wow, we left the kitchen in some state. Everything would be flung into the basin and once we sprinkled Daz or Omo on top of the greasy plates. Ma later explained that Quix was what was used to wash the dishes, not the clothes detergent.

The opening music to the R.T.E. radio show "Dear Frankie" always transports me back to those hurried lunch hours. "Whow, Whow, Whow ,Whow,Whow, Whaomh, droned the lazy Trumpet and the problems on these lunch time shows really captivated the nation.

"Well I'm not sure who is the real culprit is here," Frankie Byrne would say in her deep smokers voice, "but waiting on a proposal of marraige for

Chapter 12

35 years seems a little bit of a long wait to me, so Mary in County Mayo, what you really need to do is get tough and ask this fella of yours out straight, what his intentions are, good, bad, or indifferent." Ma would interject if she was listening, "Mary, get F'in rid of him now, and get yourself a Jaysus life Mary," she would shout at the radio. Ma never sat down to listen, she stood at the sink and listened happily as she washed and washed, peeled and peeled, cooked and cooked for us all. The Kennedy's of Castlerosse was another lunch time show at the time.

In later summers Gerry "Garter" Madden, sometimes brought the "Zetor" Tractor home, but P.J. didn't allow us to travel along the public road with him in the cab, too much potential for messing and distraction. This tractor was the Aston Martin of tractors, a full glass enclosed cab with, wait for it...a radio! Any chance we got to drive it on the farm we loved it.

The Zetor Tractor - made in Czechoslovakia

Going to work for P.J. Jones

After our first week of back breaking weeding, we got paid in the late Friday afternoon as we finished up and gathered in the big Green shed. P.J. came out of the kitchen door clasping a handful of white envelopes with our names, our hours, and totals all written in biro on the front. My first week's wages in the summer of 1970 was 15 shillings and we were rich. By 1972 it had risen to the princely sum of £2.50. The split was £2.00 for Ma, with me and Noel getting to keep 50 pence. Just past decimalization in 1971, this 50p was worth the old ten shillings. As an extra treat on pay night, Ma would bring us home a can of coke and a full packet of McVities home-wheat chocolate biscuits each from the supermarket in Northside. These we duly scoffed them all in one sitting. We only shared the last of the biscuits with the brothers and sisters, when we couldn't eat any more ourselves.

After weeding the drills of cabbage, next up were the drills of spuds. These were only done once, because when the spuds started growing the weeds among them had no chance. Pretty soon the first cabbages were ready for cutting for market and this was great stuff.

The morning of the first cabbage cutting, P. J. arrived into the big shed and started stacking up old empty 10-10-20 Net Nitrogen bags. We stood a little bemused, but Jerry Heeney and Johnny Farrell started doing the same because they knew what they were required for. Summer nights brought heavy dews and the cabbage leaves would hold all the water, hence the old Nitrate bags.

P.J. gathered us up in a circle and went into demonstration mode. Pre-cutting four separate lengths of twine he proceeded to roll one bag around his leg and tie them in place with two pieces of twine on each leg. One at crotch height and the other just under the knee. We thought he looked hilarious and we giggled and tittered as he strutted around like a cowboy who had just lost his horse. Tommy "Egg" Kavanagh was pulling faces, so was Jerry Heeney, just to get us younger lads going.

P.J. was not amused and the crosser he got the more we laughed. Our laughter however was going to be short lived. Moore's truck would be arriving at lunchtime to collect 250 dozen cabbage (3000 heads) and we hadn't started yet. We didn't have to travel too far because the front road field beside the grass tennis court was our destination. Johnny Farrell drove ahead in the Massey 165 pulling a trailer of empty steel wire crates.

The old Massey Ferguson 165 as it looks today

Going to work for P.J.Jones

As Johnny drove the tractor he sang his songs and one of them was the "Red River Valley". He had a very nasal voice and we would be impersonating him as we went. Jerry Heeney was out on the back throwing them off at various intervals. These crates held two dozen cabbages. The lighter lads were given the job of cutting the cabbages and piling them into a center furrow as we moved forward about six drills at a time.

When the cutting started, there was a demonstration from P.J. "Firstly," he explained "we won't be cutting every head out of the drill, only the ones that are big enough." Using his hand he placed it on the head to show us the size he wanted. "Next" he said, "When swinging the blade, keep you eyes open for someone too close to you getting in your way. If you are not sure, do not swing the knife, it's very sharp and it could cut someones arm off. Lastly," he said, and just then he did a bit of a high pitched throat clearance, "Ahuuummmppphhhhhttt" which caught us all by surprise and again the sniggering started.

Johnny Darcy was the absolute worst for doing this. Anything started him off imitating and sniggering. One of his favourite sayings when anything funny was going on was, "Nip! Nip!" muttered under his breathe. I did my best to control the laughter but my face was roaring red as I coughed my way out of it. "Lastly" he repeated slowly, and demonstrated as he spoke "When cutting the head from the stalk still rooted in the ground, don't cut too low into the soil or you will break your wrist. If you cut too high I will lose cabbages leaves and you might lose your fingers, now stop behaving like school girls and get to work." P.J. Jones never used bad language.

As we waded through the cabbages, they were crated carefully, ensuring the butt faced outwards and so protecting the head which faced inwards. Once a crate was filled with 24 cabbages it was left behind for Johnny

Chapter 12

Farrell and Jerry Heeney who had looped back behind us in the tractor and trailer. The bigger lads, Tommy Kavanagh and Gerry Madden threw up the full crates while Jerry Heeney stacked them. I loved this work and I felt like a jungle traveller hacking my way through the dense undergrowth. I was very good, never missing a swing with the sharp bladed knife.

As I mentioned this front road field was close to the grass tennis court. During the hot summer months, Mrs Jones and her friends would sometimes play tennis while we were working close by. These "older" women bouncing around in tennis shorts and tops were a welcome sight for us testosterone charged youths. Our very first glimpses of "eye candy," so to speak.

After the morning cabbage cutting, it wasn't unusual for us to go out after lunch and cut another 100 dozen or so, if a late afternoon collection from Moores' was required. When we started cutting cauliflowers it was the same story only we had to be very careful not to damage the head itself. Cutting cauliflower involved an extra piece and again this was demonstrated by P.J. When the head was cut at the base, the leaves then had to be trimmed while you held the head in your hand. The trick was to leave enough leaves around the head to give it protection in the crate. One time, somebody decided to use the knife blade to pull back the leaves to inspect the size of the head. Unfortunately the head was being nicked by the tip of the knife blade and when P.J. spotted a complete line of "destroyed" cauliflowers, he blew a fuse. He gathered us all around and yes, there was another demonstration.

When the cutting of the cabbages and cauliflowers started there was a small perk, as you got to bring a few home for the house. On my first Friday to bring some cabbages home, I came in by bicycle. I loaded

243

the plastic bag full of cabbages onto the handle bars and I walked the bicycle, balancing the bag as I went along. I left Jones' by the front gate and I turned right for home. The first house I passed was old Mrs Mc-Guirk's small red cottage. She was a widow and a very small old woman who wore a dark navy old fashion pinny. P.J. had given me some cabbage to drop into her.

This was the first of many visits I would make to Mrs McGuirk. One day as we got talking, she ended up playing me some of her Doris Day records! She knew my grand father Bill Cooley well because she bought coal from him. On down the road from Mr's McGuirk's cottage, I met Ned Fowler, chewing his pipe and sitting beside the milk churns outside the gate of his small dairy farm which was on the left hand side.

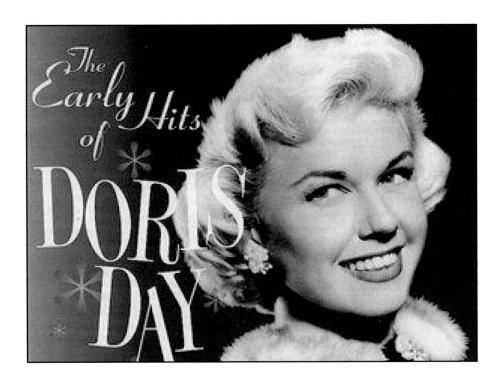

Fowler's farm on the Clonshaugh road

Later, when I started attending Belcamp College in 1970, I saw Mr Fowler most days because Tommy Kavanagh,(the same one who was working with me on Jones' farm), lived across the road from him. When I started in first year I would call for Tommy on my way to school. He was a distant cousin of mine and was two years ahead of me in Belcamp. He lived with his mother, Cathleen Kavanagh, his grand aunt Sissy and her husband Jack Fitzsimons. Their cottage was pretty as a picture.

Fitzsimon's cottage facing Fowler's

Going to work for P.J. Jones

Ned Fowler used to call out as I headed off on my way to school, "That young Cooley, he has brains to burn!" Ned's youngest son Stephen "Skitcher" Fowler was a great character and you could hear him singing in the milking shed at the top of his voice. "Now here's a song that hit the top, it's Elvis Presley and I'm all shook up, now dig that man from Tennesse, it's Jim Reeves, but it's really me." Stephen Fowler in my mind represented what people from places like Turnapin and Clonshaugh were all about back then. Hard workers but always up for a bit of fun.

Just past Fowler's, staying on the left I passed by Gunning's farm and they mostly grew flowers. My two soldiers from the "Battle of Turnapin Lane" lived here. These were the two brothers, Christy and Gerard, and they were around my age. The younger one Gerard, often spoke to me as he came in and out of Fowler's with Stephen's young son Damian, whom we all called "Gooks". These two Gunning brothers, along with young Damian would become great friends with myself and my younger brother Noel in our later teenage years and we will hear more about them in later stories.

Gunnings Farm - Formerly known as Kelly's and McCormack's

Chapter 12

Now scooting along on the bike on the one pedal, I carried on heading for Turnapin with my bag of cabbages. I passed by Andrews' modern bungalow on the right then on down the road only to meet the first big obstacle which was "Jolly's Hill." This was a really big hill and I had to dismount because it was that steep. Before tackling it, I repositioned the spreading plastic bag of cabbages and had it sitting well balanced on the bike. Speeding cars and lorries were a huge problem while negotiating Jolly's hill. These would speed up and down and around the blind corners so you really had to have your wits about you.

View of Jolly's Hill looking towards Turnapin Lane

Going to work for P.J.Jones

Once up the hill I headed on along the road, passing the yard entrance to McKenna's big house on the left. It didn't have a gate, but it really didn't need one, especially when there were a few Doberman Pinchers lurking around the yard up at the house. Up ahead was Howard's field on the right and then I passed the modern looking semi-detached house that the lady golfer Mary McKenna lived in. Next door to Mary lived the Gannons who were related to her.

On again for a few hundred yards I travelled around "Tinker's corner". I only ever remember once seeing a horse drawn Tinker's Wagon parked up at Tinker's corner. They got their water at Curran's well and fresh eggs from Dolly McGuirk. After that they moved up to the bank along McKennas field on the back road.

The Tinker's corner looking back towards Maddens and McGuirks

Chapter 12

By the time I passed Madden's corner and I got to Heeney's gap, I was well and truly knackered. The gap itself was narrow and it was near to impossible to get through on a bicycle with a bag of vegetables in tow. It was best to drop the bag to the ground, drag it through on it's own and then follow along with the bicycle.

The gap ran along the outer wire fence of the sewerage pump station and as I manouvered the bicycle my knuckles took a bashing. Oh yes, just what I needed at the end of a hard days work, but it was worth it. Ma was always delighted to see the bag of fresh heads of cabbage. This would the first of many trips home with a "carry out" of vegetables from Jones farm.

Back on Jones' farm it will come as no surprise to anyone that I started getting a bit of flack from P.J. over talking too much. He once remarked that if I could work as hard as I could talk, he could let all the other lads go! Hands up yes I was a bit "chatty". After mastering weeding and cutting cabbages with the sharp knives, the next big event for me was learning to drive.

My big chance came when the potatoes were ripe for harvesting. P.J. was a very progressive farmer and the labour intensive way of hand picking the spuds was old hat. He duly bought this massive machine that lifted up a complete drill as it went along, turned it over, spread and scattered the soil and spuds up onto a rotating platform. The huge machine was bright red and it looked like something from the 'Thunderbirds' Television series.

It had big spinning wheels and gadgets galore on board. This machine was the "Cats-Pyjamas," and was very much the cradle to grave potato picking solution. All it was short of having on board was a canteen and toilets.

When it came time to get this machine into service it was always a very big event. It was stored in the big road shed beside the house which opened out on to the public road. Since it required a tractor to pull it out of the shed, it had to be done quickly because general road traffic would be held up. With it being out of service since the previous year there was a fair bit of preparation involved to get all the parts checked and oiled for the new season ahead. A lot of this work was carried out before it left the shed and this work was always closely supervised by P.J. himself.

It had a platform for standing on and this was manned by at least six people who picked the spuds, then dropped them into a channel that directed them into a bag. When the bag was filled up to four stone weight, Johnny Farrell tied it off and just dropped it off onto the ground to be picked up later by tractor and trailer. There was a little "gizmo" gun that twisted the wire to seal the four stone potato bags and god help us if that went missing. Everybody obssessed about it, especially P.J. himself. "Where's the bag Tier?, Who has the bag Tier ?, Who had it last?," and Jesus, God help you if you were named as the "The last person I saw with that was." No amount of explaining would suffice, you would just have to find it and present it to Johnny Farrell, the main potato bag tie-up man.

This massive machine was connected to the tractor by a tow bar and it was powered by the P.T.O at the rear. It also had some hydraulic hoses which were also connected to the tractor.

Before the harvester went near the drill of potatoes, the tops of the plants had to be trimmed off. This was done with one of the many attachments that were hooked into the back of a tractor. This particular time Tommy Kavanagh was trimming ahead of us in the Massey-Ferguson 165, and when he was coming around the headland not too far from us, he was grinning and waving not watching where he was going. We looked again but Tommy and tractor-trimmers had just disappeared.

He was just gone, there one second and gone the next. He had gone down into a huge field ditch. We all called out to P.J. who was driving the Massey-Ferguson 135 which was pulling the harvester. He stopped the tractor and leaped out to where Tommy had been seen last. We all followed on to catch up and found Tommy, in the tractor, wedged in the ditch, tractor on it's side and still grinning up at us. Thankfully Tommy wasn't hurt and before long we had pulled the tractor free using the powerful Zetor.

Going to work for P.J.Jones

Massey Ferguson 711 Potato Harvester

Meanwhile back on the harvester, my big chance to drive was coming. P.J. restarted the Massey 135 and then it happened. He jumped out leaving it at a crawling speed and asked me to get in and steer it. I was thrilled, all I had to do was to keep the wheels centered in the drill furrows. Things were going well until we got near to the end of the drill. With about 20 feet to go to the headland, I started to panic, and started to lock the wheels into a right turn. Before long we were bobbing up and down as I cut across the drills, everyone hanging on for dear life. P.J. jumped from the harvester platform and was running towards me shouting and waving. He jumped into the tractor cab, pushing me to one side. After it was stopped I explained he hadn't showed me the end of drill routine. He agreed it was his fault and yes, there was another demonstration. After that I was the official potato harvester driver for the summer of 1970. Being the driver had its benefits but it also had it's drawbacks. Firstly, you were isolated, so no fun to be had messing with the others. Secondly, when P.J. wasn't about, incoming "sniggers" (small potatoes) thrown by your jealous comrades would bounce off your crouching back, neck and head.

Of all the many stories I could relate about working in the fields for P.J Jones, one in particular sticks out in my mind. Out in the fields there were no toilets so the many ditches around were our only outlet and in general it was only peeing. One time, one of our group, lets call him Mister X, decided that he just had to go for a number two. Now the secret here was to slip away unnoticed and do what you had to do. With your trousers down around your ankles, way down in a ditch, you were very very vulnerable. As Mister X slipped away quietly, he was spotted by Johnny Darcy. The alarm was quietly raised and an ambush was on the cards. The probable location of Mr X, down in the ditch was ascertained and after a two minute lull to give him time to settle down, what I can only describe as a scene from the "bombing of Baghdad" was unleashed. Balls of muck rained down from the sky on the poor unfortunate. Amid a lot of shouting and cursing he eventually climbed back up out of the ditch much the worse for wear. He had a graze over his eye as he emerged bleeding and groggy. Just at that very moment, Mr Jones appeared in the field. He was livid. He lined us up and read us the riot act, horse play would not be tolerated. "Somebody could have lost an eye," He shouted. It was the last time we ever did that.

Postscript : I recorded P.J. Jones in 2004 for my "Voices of Santry" local history project. He had always blamed me for starting the muck throwing incident. I told him it was Johnny Darcy. I also told him that his pipe smoke drifting on the wind gave us a prior warning that he was about, he laughed, and yes he is still a gentleman.

Epilogue

I first heard the word epilogue on an American television series called Quincy. He was a medical detective who always solved the case. It was introduced in a really deep dramatic american law enforcement voice. In the case of "Turn at the Pine Trees" what really should happen is a "To be continued" would appear across our screens. The good news is, there will be more.

The years will move on to 1975 until I sit my Leaving Certificate in Belcamp. The dreaded "Teen" years meets the Glamrock 1970's. At this stage most of them are already written with the illustrations well on the way. The very first story in this sequel of sorts is all about my very first day in Belcamp College. The Cloghran Youth Club (O.L.Q.Y.) The Belcamp discos and the Dublin Airport Legion of Mary are also in there. There will be another twelve stories all interwoven into the changes that continued to affect Turnapin and the people who lived there with me.

I can't sign off without saying a big thank you to my youngest son Sean, who has worked very closely with me on this book. Putting it simply, without him I was lost. Chapter 8 is his triumph on graphics.

Back with the book in hand, I leave you with a small poem I wrote which sums up my feelings on the way things went in Turnapin lane, I would like to dedicate it and the very first signed copy of my book to Pat Ingoldsby, my streets of Dublin pal.

I read this to him in Westmoreland street and he liked it. Just like my Turnapin lane, his small village of Malahide has suffered greatly at the hands of the plunderers. Keep the faith Pat.

255

Ode To Turnapin Lane

I sometimes walk and I sometimes wander,
through places now in derelict slumber.
Where once lay fields of rolling green,
with purple thistle in a country scene.

They now bear witness to noise and rumble,
buried and lost in this concrete jungle.
They've humbled this place, they've stolen it's treasure,
covered it up with blocks well measured.
They dug it up and they scattered it round,
all for profit, pound on pound.

Was Turnapin Lane just unlucky,
It's thirty six cottages once so plucky.
Carleys gone, Geraghtys too,
All vanished, destroyed, leaving no clue.

The same of Hillfarm, once so smelly,
where the flies fed on the dead pig's belly.
The Tinker's corner, McGuirks as well,
Lie lost forever in this concrete hell.

When you read my book, it will help you remember,
My words and pictures from a childhood tender.
Though the places and people are long since gone,
The spirit of Turnapin still burns strong.

Gerry Cooley 2010